HITTING *the* ROCK

CHRIS MAGGS

Purple Plum Books

Published in Great Britain 2011 by Purple Plum Books

ISBN No: 978-0-9570068-0-5

Typeset in Palatino Linotype

An environmentally friendly book printed and bound in England by
www.printondemand-worldwide.com

This book is made entirely of chain-of-custody materials.

Purple Plum Books
www.purpleplumbooks.co.uk

To Fiona, without whom
the world would be a lonely
(and less organised) place

JESUS HAS CHEMO

INTRODUCTION

The word 'cancer' frightens people. Despite massive progress in treatment techniques, it still carries the ominous threat of death. Cancer covers a range of illnesses around the central theme of your body's own cells malfunctioning and becoming a threat to health and ultimately life itself. Causes are largely unknown. Though there are some obvious influences like smoking and asbestos, what triggers a cell to turn traitor is unclear. It can happen to fit as well as unfit people. It does not discriminate by age, sex or religion. Some types strike quickly, others spread slowly. Some can be treated successfully, others cannot. If you believe in luck, it is just the luck of the draw. If you believe in a higher force directing every action of nature, it is the will of the 'gods'. Either way, it seems a cruel and unfair world that deals out such problems and leaves us to cope as best we can.

This is the story of our cancer journey. We're not making any claims that our experiences are any more interesting than the next person's but we have tried to be honest and give you the whole story, drawing a modest veil only over the most intimate parts of married life (though to be honest there's not much to draw a veil over given the effects of the cancer and its treatment). In doing so we share with you our faith struggles as well. We believe in God - a good God who loves us - which throws up some interesting questions when faced with the devastating reality of cancer.

Each section begins with an email that my wife, Fiona, sent to keep people updated on progress. The first two emails were

1

just to friends who were working in the USA for six months because at that stage we did not know there was anything to keep people updated about! The emails and their dates are unchanged from the originals and tell the story as it unfolded from Fiona's perspective. I have then added my own thoughts about the things that were going on and the way it affected me and my faith.

A little bit of family background will probably help as we go through. Fiona is an occupational therapist and we have been married for 21 years when the story begins in April 2005. We have three children. Tim is 17 and studying for his AS levels, Luke is 14 and Hannah is 9. We live just south of Birmingham. I work as an actuary in the never-dull world of pensions.

PART ONE

JESUS HAS CHEMO

FROM: **FIONA MAGGS**
DATE: **15 APRIL 2005**
TO: **AARON AND DIANE IN THE USA**
SUBJECT: **HELLO**

It's great to hear from you and catch up with all that you are doing. It is odd to think that you are so far away but technology means that we can be in touch so easily.

Life has carried on much the same as usual in the Maggs household (although I have bought a couple of new suitcases for our adventure!). It was back to school this week. Hannah had a big dose of schoolitis on Tuesday but felt better once we started walking to school. She has now moved her swimming lessons to Saturday morning as she is now doing her bronze.

Chris is not feeling too well and still has the cough that he has had since Christmas. Work is also very busy and he is not sleeping well so all these are contributing to him feeling a bit 'off'! I have had a really busy week at work as well. I had the first session of a new venture that I am involved in setting up at the hospital. This is a patient user group for rheumatology patients. It is something quite new and exciting and the latest thing that we are meant to be setting up (government initiative). The first group went really well and people seem to be pleased with what we are doing. It involves more hours for me though.

Well I have just noticed the time. I need to go and fetch Tim from work. He seems to be getting on well and they are happy with him. His chatty nature is OK working in a shop.

Will be in touch again.
Miss you, Fiona

LOOKING BACK

It's funny how you look back sometimes and see things in a different way. The email was just a routine summary of family news to our friends who were spending six months in the USA. The "adventure" referred to was our planned trip to fly over and stay with them in August. As committed caravaners we had never travelled beyond France for our holidays so this was to be a major excursion for us. As it turned out our big adventure was to be in a different direction altogether.

I couldn't tell you when my cough started. It probably just sneaked in slowly over a few days but by Christmas 2004 it was bad enough to be annoying. But what drove me to the doctor's in January was not the cough, which I dismissed as a winter cold, but a pain in my shoulder. The doctor diagnosed a muscle tear and gave me exercises and anti-inflammatory tablets for a month. They seemed to do the trick as the pain disappeared for a while. But when the tablets finished the pain came back so I returned to the doctor's and got some more. Again the pain went and again it came back when the tablets had finished. And all the time the cough persisted, slowly getting worse. I remember trying to do a presentation as part of my work and having to apologise for the constant coughing breaks.

As April progressed my health got steadily worse. I sometimes woke up in the night drenched in sweat. I was getting headaches, losing weight and was not sleeping well. I started taking paracetamol each night but sometimes the coughing got such a grip I could not stop it. Twice I had been retching over the toilet thinking I would be sick but it did not happen. Despite all this, I had no sense of being seriously ill and was continuing to work normally. It was Fiona, with a nose for the medical, who added all the symptoms together and felt uncomfortable with the total.

She persuaded me to see the doctor again on 26 April, coming with me to make sure I gave him the whole story. She thought it may be TB and the doctor asked questions around this as well. He decided a chest X-ray was needed and gave me a form to take to the hospital the following morning. He said he did not think it was cancer and I made a joke of it, never considering it a serious possibility. Nevertheless, the discomfort at night and the consequent lack of sleep convinced me that getting it sorted must be top priority.

And so the journey began, not with a dramatic fanfare or sudden catastrophe but by tiny unremarkable steps. We slid into what was to become the most dramatic period of our lives without even noticing it had started, which is probably the way I'd have liked it to have been anyway. I would not describe myself as an optimist, my motto generally being, "Things can always get worse," but I certainly do not panic. Regrettably, this is not down to some super-spiritual quality of character so much as a rather naïve expectation that things will sort themselves out. I am one of those people who tend to ignore the light on the dashboard in the hope that it will go away. I never try and mend anything immediately either, in case it sorts itself out first. Surprisingly, some things do resolve themselves without any intervention but, perhaps less surprisingly, most do not and I have suffered the consequences of leaving things too long on more than one occasion.

Applying this principle to my own health, I am generally reluctant to see the doctor, preferring suffering to taking tablets. I take it for granted that my body will fix any internal problems with limited intervention. Such a philosophy helps me stay calm when anyone with more sense would see the potential dangers ahead!

FROM:	**FIONA MAGGS**
DATE:	**30 APRIL 2005**
TO:	**AARON AND DIANE IN THE USA**
SUBJECT:	**A BIT OF NEWS FOR YOU**

Hi all,

Hope you are OK. I just wanted to bring you up to date on Chris' health. I mentioned that he was not well in a previous email. He went back to the doctors this week and was sent for an urgent chest x-ray. Last night we discovered that this has shown up a shadow on his lung and so now he has to go to the hospital for further tests. We are waiting for an urgent appointment which should be in 1-2 weeks. It's good that we now have a reason why Chris has been feeling awful and gradually getting worse as each week went by. There are various things it could be and so now we just wait and see. We will let you know when we know more.

Fiona.

CASTING A SHADOW

I generally hate hospitals. My previous experience of them (as a visitor only) is that they are old fashioned rambling buildings with odd smells and too many people. The Alexandra Hospital in Redditch did not fit my stereotype. It was modern, clean and not too big. To my surprise I found the X-ray Department easily, booked in and settled down for a long wait. Again, I was disappointed as I was called fairly quickly to another area and then into the X-ray room shortly afterwards. The staff were pleasant and efficient as they invited me to slump myself over the machine. After a brief wait to check the image had developed I was free to go. I returned home to change, then went off to work.

I had not mentioned the X-ray to anyone at work but my consistent cough was obvious enough as it interfered with all my conversations and telephone calls. Months later colleagues told me they thought I had been looking unwell for a while but at the time they did not say anything. The office environment, or ours at any rate, does not encourage social care and concern. This is not deliberate policy. In fact I have been impressed by the level of concern that people in the office have shown since I 'came out' with a serious illness. The people do care and so does 'the corporation' in its widest sense. Yet the nature of day to day business leaves little room for casual chat and personal enquiries. I am equally guilty in this respect, my only effort to make such space being the occasional quick lunch with a colleague before we throw ourselves back into the grinding wheels of commerce. Perhaps the experiences of this particular journey will make me better at taking the time needed to support others. I hope so.

Fiona called the doctor's a couple of days after the X-ray to arrange an appointment to discuss the results. They said they would check if they had come through and get back to us but instead the doctor turned up on our doorstep at noon. Unfortunately, I was working in Bristol so Fiona arranged for us to see him at the surgery at 6 p.m. Needless to say, Fiona was most concerned that the news was grim given the doctor's eagerness to see us. I added to her stress by leaving work later than I should and meeting her at the surgery just after the allotted time. Somehow, when I am in work mode, every minute counts and I tend to leave the office with only just enough time to get wherever I am supposed to be. (The process is a little more complex actually, and involves an element of self-deception. Knowing that I am bad at getting places ahead of time I deliberately plan to leave in good time. However, I do so in the knowledge that I will inevitably fail to leave at the planned time and, leaving late, will just about make it. So it was for the doctor's appointment.)

The news was that the X-ray showed a shadow on the lung. The doctor was keen to point out that this could mean several things, some relatively minor, others major. He did a good job to help us understand the position and was obviously most concerned that we would be worried. Actually, we were not. We understood that it was too early to assume the worst and just wanted to get on with the process of finding out what it was. I had had some particularly bad nights with coughing fits and felt that the sooner we could progress things the better.

The doctor said the NHS 'fast track' system would be quicker than any private medical help so we agreed to stick with that. And so it proved to be all the way along. Despite the common perception that the NHS is falling apart we found the treatment for cancer was always good. I guess this is because cancer treatment is given priority, which is down to both Government targets and the popular view of cancer as a terror disease. In that sense, I suppose, I was fortunate.

When we got home we shared the news with our children. It never seemed appropriate to hide it from them. It was probably nothing serious after all. But we gave them the range of possibilities. It happened that the same day we got this news my brothers, sister and respective partners all came round for a meal, unaware of any particular problems or that I had gone for an X-ray. We fully intended to let them know what had happened, though finding an ideal moment to mention you have a shadow on your lung can be tricky. The opportunity forced itself upon us very early in proceedings after Hannah bounced up to one of my sisters-in-law and announced loudly, "My daddy's going to die".

We shared the situation with other close family and also with some people in our church. For us, church has always been extended family and it was natural for us to let the people who cared for us know what was going on. On the other hand, I was concerned not to start a riot! It was just a shadow on an X-ray and may amount to nothing much so I asked that the news should not go any further at this stage. I must have expressed myself badly because the message that went around was that I didn't want to talk about it. So for a while even those who knew said nothing to me and I began to wonder if anyone cared.

The misunderstanding soon resolved itself but a similar phenomenon was encountered a number of times over the next few months. We found that quite a few people felt it more sensitive to say nothing rather than ask how things were going. I can understand why because I might have been the same, and probably have been on occasions. There is a fear that if things are going badly then asking the person about it will only upset them. From the other side I can see it differently. Those who ask are the ones who come across as showing concern, whether things are going badly or not. It is another lesson I need to remember and apply myself.

Around this time we had one of our regular church Leadership Team meetings. These took place in the home of a couple on the team on a Friday evening. My role was to make sure we got through the agenda by roughly ten o'clock – an informal sort of chairman. I apologised at the beginning for my coughing but as we progressed it got noticeably worse and soon I could not manage a sentence without breaking into another fit. I retired to the kitchen to get a drink of water and sit quietly until it calmed down. It didn't work. I was still barking away so loudly and gasping for breath in between that it was disturbing for everyone else, not just in terms of the noise but their concern for me. Instead of continuing the meeting the team gathered around and prayed for us. Then Fiona and I went home and found some relief in cough mixture.

I did not rejoin those leadership meetings for many months and looking back it was the first thing I can remember not being able to do. I have always been fairly confident in taking on things and am active in lots of areas. I don't think of myself as outgoing but there is an inner self-belief that I credit mainly to my father. I don't know if he actually said it but in my head I can hear him say, "You're a Maggs, you can do anything". Of course, it is not entirely true. I'm hopeless at practical things and I've learned to give a wide berth to plumbing but as a motivational statement it has worked for me in many situations. So not being able to do something, in this case be part of the leadership team meetings, was a dent in my self-perception.

At least I was continuing to work, though I found myself wanting to stay in the office rather than go out to client meetings, the opposite of my usual preference. Meanwhile, the doctor had set up an appointment for me with a respiratory specialist consultant.

FROM:	FIONA MAGGS
DATE:	10 MAY 2005
TO:	OUR NETWORK OF FRIENDS AND FAMILY
SUBJECT:	UPDATE ON CHRIS

We have been to see the Doctor this morning and things are moving pretty quickly. Chris is to have a bronchoscopy tomorrow afternoon (a look down into his lungs under sedation!) and then a CT scan on either Thursday/Friday. We are booked to go back and see the consultant on Monday afternoon hopefully for a diagnosis. He did seem to think it was serious and mentioned possibly Lymphoma.

Please pray for Chris tomorrow afternoon. We don't know what time as there is a list, (we don't know where he is on that list + someone more urgent may be done first) but it is sometime between 2pm & 5pm. It is not a pleasant experience and Chris does not really like hospitals. We will have more idea of what comes next after Monday.

Fiona.

TESTS AND TESTES

Fiona's medical background proved invaluable from the start. I've heard it said that people retain only a small fraction of the information that doctors give them and my own experience backs this up. I walked out of this first respiratory consultation with very little understanding of what was going on, mystified by medical words and unsure who half the people I'd spoken to were. Fortunately Fiona is different and could recall it all in detail.

It does not help that consultants have teams of registrars, so when you think you have an appointment with a particular doctor you actually see someone else who is working with them. They give you their name and you try to remember it, though it turns out you will never see them again. You start getting into a conversation, giving medical history and so on, when the consultant breezes in and starts again from the beginning, as if the registrar is not even there. Mind you, this is better than the occasions when the registrar has to keep leaving the room to consult the consultant, leaving you wondering if you just happened to get someone on work experience.

We came back home mid-morning and sat and discussed it. Fiona explained it all to me. Not only could she remember the medical terms, she could also spell them! At this stage it was still a question of finding things out so we were able to talk quite dispassionately. At least, that was the theory. We were talking about the need to cancel a speaking engagement I had later in the month when I suddenly burst into tears. Fiona followed and we hugged.

It was as if an emotional river had been running along just under the surface and, without warning, had broken out through a weak point in my defences. And that weak point happened to be me admitting that I could not do something. Fiona and I feel able to cope with virtually everything but there was a realisation that we may not be able to cope with this. It was good to let it out and wallow in that deep sense of inadequacy that underlies the human spirit. But we were soon back in control of ourselves, popping the cork on the emotional bottle once more.

I went to work in the afternoon, needing to clear up the urgent things and cancel a few meetings. I told my office head what was going on, and also one of my colleagues, but nobody else at work.

By this point the number of friends and family who knew what was going on was too big to handle with phone calls, so Fiona started doing email updates. It proved to be a very helpful way of keeping people informed and the messages spread out over time as some people passed them on to friends and acquaintances far and wide. And as the information was dispersed into cyberspace through the modern wonder of modems and microchips, so prayers were being despatched through ancient and even more wonderful spiritual channels, direct to God. Prayer will probably always remain a mystery to us, at least this side of heaven, but the knowledge of such prayers and the care and concern that they express was a tangible comfort to us. I believe God heard those prayers and allowed us to feel their warmth.

I've long thought doctors have a lot in common with garage mechanics. They are both in the business of fixing things and generally adopt a similar approach, gradually eliminating various possibilities until they are sure what the problem is. So I found myself up on the ramps, as it were, undergoing a series of gradually more intrusive tests. First up, quite literally, was the bronchoscopy. This involved sticking a camera up my nose and down into my lungs to see if there was any damage. Fortunately this is done under sedation, which meant that although I was conscious, I did not remember anything. It is an odd concept. It felt like I went to sleep and woke up when it was all over, like an anaesthetic, but apparently I was awake throughout. It reminds me of those time travel science-fiction films where, towards the end, the characters get sent back to the beginning after being told they will remember nothing of what has happened - except that in the films nobody gets a camera up their nose.

Next was the CT Scan, which was not too bad except for the needle they had to put in my arm. Then we were back to see the consultant again. We prayed together, for God's peace, before going. Neither of us prayed that it would all be okay or that the shadow would have gone. It did not seem right to do so.

Our appointment was at 2.30 p.m. on 16 May and we arrived on time. As before, I was weighed and had my blood pressure taken. The Nurse Specialist checked my reaction to the 'Heaf test' done on my arm previously and confirmed that I did not have TB. Then we waited. And waited. And waited. Being very British, it got to 4 p.m. before Fiona politely asked if there was a problem. It turned out that they had booked five appointments for the consultant at 2 p.m. and he was still working through them. This is an interesting feature of the NHS booking system, attempted temporary time distortion in order to get more appointments in than is physically possible, the only casualties being the patients held in the time-space void otherwise known as the waiting room.

To add insult to injury we were subjected to daytime TV, which seemed to comprise continuous programmes about property development. Unable to change channel, most of us pretended not to watch but our only other distraction was a table of leaflets on a range of respiratory disorders. Since I didn't know what I had I was loath to pick one out in case it was not very nice, so I sat and pretended not to watch the property development programmes instead.

We were seen eventually. At least, we were taken into the consultant's office, where he ignored us for five minutes while discussing another patient with one of his registrars. Then he said hello and set about reading my notes for a few minutes more before informing us that my CT Scan results were not there and sending us back to the waiting area while they were found.

A little while later we returned to his room and at last we got the information we'd been waiting nearly three hours for. The CT Scan revealed a 7cm tumour. The consultant said it did not look like a lymphoma after all, though it still could be. As well as pressing on the lung it was also near a blood vessel so he thought surgery was unlikely. One end was near my left shoulder and this was likely to have been causing the pains that took me to the doctor back in January. I was still getting aches in my shoulder from time to time.

He explained that the next step to investigate the tumour further would be a needle biopsy. This would involve sticking a needle into my chest to get some cells out of the tumour for analysis. It would be a week before this could happen and the results would take another week or so. After that I would probably be referred on to another specialist so it looked like three weeks before any treatment would be decided. I found this daunting as my health had been deteriorating quickly over the previous few days. I was easily exhausted and coughing rapidly brought on hot flushes.

We left the hospital with this information and a sense of frustration that we still had to wait so long with many questions still unanswered. "Is it malignant?" was at the top of the list.

Fiona had intended to send an email round to inform people of progress but our computer had a virus and was at the computer hospital itself, an irony lost on us at the time. Instead there were lots of telephone calls. Despite the frustration and continued poor health, we remained fairly calm and tried to look on the positive side. Even though a tumour had been diagnosed, which was worse than some of the other options, at least we knew more than before. It was progress towards a full diagnosis and treatment. And it might still turn out to be nothing too serious.

Certainly that was my thinking as I went into work the following afternoon. But I noticed the difference in my condition compared with the previous week. Trying to control my cough made it hard even to carry out a conversation. My office head agreed I should not attempt to come into work again until I was better. I went through all the outstanding jobs with a colleague, warning him that it could be two or three months before I returned.

It was a great relief to let these responsibilities go since I knew I could not cope with them but it was also an emotional milestone. When I realised I was too ill to work it made me feel like crying again, though being in the office I operated the stiff upper lip policy. I didn't want to be useless and the realisation that I was, hurt me somewhere very deep inside.

There was another test to fit in before the needle biopsy. In conversation with the consultant he had thought it worth checking for lumps in my testicles so an ultrasound was booked. Ever since Adam and Eve we've had a primitive instinct to cover up certain parts and it was with some trepidation that I made my way to this appointment. Of course, we were all very civilised and grown up about it but, even so! After introductions it was trousers down and up on the couch while the doctor checked over the goods with his sensor. No sign of lumps so everything seemed to be okay there. When he had finished I had to wipe off the gel but it wasn't the sort of situation where you could do a thorough job. I walked off in the style of John Wayne and stopped in one of the toilets on the way out to complete the task. Hannah was horrified when I told her what the doctor had been checking. She thought it was disgusting.

FROM: **FIONA MAGGS**

DATE: **23 MAY 2005**

TO: **OUR NETWORK OF FRIENDS AND FAMILY**

SUBJECT: **TODAY AT THE HOSPITAL!**

Just to let you all know that the biopsy went OK today. Everything happened as planned and the follow up x-ray after an hour showed no problem. We are back home and ready to wait now for the results which will take 4-5 days to come. We are expecting that we will get an appointment to see the doctor next Tuesday.

Thank you all again for praying for us. I have especially felt very calm today and feel that I am experiencing the 'peace that passes understanding'.

Fiona

IN-PATIENTS AND IMPATIENCE

A couple of days before the needle biopsy I was at a prayer morning at our church. We covered a number of topics but at the end we prayed for personal needs and I asked them to pray for me. I don't like having a lot of attention. In a group I prefer to observe than be observed but the situation seemed serious enough for me to ask for specific prayer. One or two people prayed and I appreciated their thoughtful expressions of concern and their desire for God to be with me.

And then our friend Sarah prayed. I do not recall what she said but the words resonated with me somewhere deep and popped the cork off that bottle again. Generally my faith reflects my personality in that it takes place more in my head than my heart but this was a moment when prayer seemed to go beyond words and touched my soul. It felt like spirit stood alongside spirit in the presence of God and no language comes close to moments like that. I reached for the tissues and blubbed!

The practicalities of life will insist on forcing themselves back upon us and I had to leave quickly afterwards as I was late to pick my son Luke up from his tennis training. The experience was only a few minutes within the context of many stressful days but, for me, moments like that were milestones along the way; markers to look back upon and know that deep within, where it matters, God is right on the spot.

The needle biopsy went smoothly and we were treated to yet more property development TV while waiting in the Discharge Lounge, the word "Lounge" presumably used to suggest something more pleasurable than a waiting room, which is basically what it was. As a temporary in-patient, I was also treated to a courtesy wheelchair for transportation between departments. Apparently there are medical reasons for this, to do with reducing the risk of blood clots. The only clot turned out to be me, or at least I felt like one as I was being pushed here and there.

It is noticeable how your status changes once you are an in-patient as opposed to an out-patient. The fact that such black and white prefixes have been allowed to remain in our politically correct society is indicative of how ingrained they are in the system. A patient's status is also determined by their means of transport. Top of the list are the patients who get wheeled around in a bed. I get this treatment later on and feel a bit of a fraud because I could have walked if asked. Next are patients who are walking but pull a drip or other device alongside them. Some hospitals have little groups of these, in various bed wear, greeting you at the main entrance doors with cigarette smoke. The wheelchair users come next, accompanied by chirpy porters who hail each other across the wards and corridors and seem to be the only ones who think it's okay to have a laugh in a hospital. And then there are the patients on foot, who can be subdivided into those who look as if they know where they are going and those who look confused, the latter either being lost or there for precisely that reason.

Status is equally important as far as staff are concerned. First there are those in uniforms, the meanings of which are coded by colours and trims so as to be a mystery to the patients. Staff not in uniform are either clerical, ranking below anyone in uniform to my uninitiated mind, or doctors, ranking above everyone, uniform or not. The way to tell doctors from clerical is, of course, the stethoscope around the neck, now far more common than the previous favourite of a white coat. Porters stand apart from all this because, although they have a uniform of sorts, they manage to wear it as if they didn't. In the pecking order, as it appears to operate, porters rank near the bottom of the staff pile (just above the contract cleaners) though they do manage to command exclusive use of certain lifts for some obscure reason.

Life carried on as we waited for the results of the needle biopsy. Tim was preparing for AS level module exams, Hannah and Luke went to stay with cousins during half term. Fiona had a birthday and as a treat we travelled to a shopping centre in Tamworth and saw Sharon Osbourne. I should point out, in the interest of maintaining street credibility, that the trip was not specifically to see Sharon Osbourne. It was just coincidence that she was filming an Asda advert there. I confess we actually went in order to find a Hobbycraft shop, which probably carries even less credibility, street or otherwise.

Healthwise things were not good. Sleeping was difficult because of the coughing and hot sweats, my voice was disappearing and I continued to lose weight and grow weaker. Every day was another day without treatment and the sooner we had a firm diagnosis the sooner something could start to be done. As it turned out, it was probably a good thing we had no idea how far away treatment would end up being.

FROM:	**FIONA MAGGS**
DATE:	**31 MAY 2005**
TO:	**OUR NETWORK OF FRIENDS AND FAMILY**
SUBJECT:	**UPDATE ON CHRIS**

Another visit to the hospital today for the results of the biopsy. Unfortunately they are inconclusive. They think that it may be a low grade malignancy but it is looking like it is one of the more rare ones and they need more to go on to decide what it is. This means that Chris now has to go to Heartlands hospital for a surgical biopsy (under anaesthetic). We are yet again waiting to hear from the surgeon with a date which will hopefully be reasonably quick and then we will have another wait for the results of that biopsy. Treatment does not seem to be getting any nearer at the moment. Chris is continuing to deteriorate and felt quite down after the appointment this morning as he just wants to get some treatment as soon as possible.

We hope we will have some more positive news to give you soon.

Love Fiona

WHAT'S THE POINT OF PRAYER?

The inconclusive result was something of a low point for me. I was philosophical at the hospital but when we got back in the car I cried again. I felt angry about having to wait longer and even complained, "What's the point in having so many people praying for you?" At the time, I wrote a short piece on how I was feeling and I've reproduced it here. Lots of questions and not a great many answers.

Do you want to get well?

These are the words of Jesus to a man who had been an invalid for 38 years. They had always struck me as strange until recently. Why would the man not want to be well? Of course he would. But it is not that simple. The question of healing is a complex one and stirs up all sorts of questions. For myself, suffering with a tumour that is pressing on my lung, the question is one I have had to ask and I admit I do not know the answer. For a man who has been living with something for 38 years the implications of immediate health are not insubstantial. There is compassion in the question. This was one of the rare occasions when Jesus went and found someone to heal them, rather than the person (or their friends) coming to him. Perhaps before healing can take place there needs to be a willingness either to come to Jesus and ask, or otherwise to be able to answer the above question positively. These are my thoughts on this subject as I ask myself the question.

1. *Loads of people are praying for me. It is humbling but I also feel a sense of responsibility to be sufficiently unwell. I find myself being reassured that I definitely have a tumour. A bit of me hopes for bad news on the histology to justify all the concerns of these people. Crazy!*

2. *What are people praying for? All sorts of things I imagine. Some will be praying for miraculous healing, others for healing through the medical profession, others for peace and/or God's presence to be with us. Who knows what else? How does God decide what to do?*

3. *What am I praying for? I have not prayed frequently or long and hard. My prayers are simple. I ask God to take the tumour away (leaving the method up to him) and I ask for courage and strength to deal with the things I am suffering. Sometimes I think I am suffering a lot. Other times I think I am making more of it than I ought. I do believe that God has relieved a lot of my pain since I was having harsh coughing attacks weeks ago, particularly at night. Now I hardly cough in the night at all and lying down seems to be the best position for me. I thank God for sleep.*

4. *A friend told me he would be happy to take me to his church, where healings take place frequently. Apparently they have had a number of cases of cancer miraculously healed. The idea of going does not appeal to me at all. It is a big and lively church and I would need to go down the front for prayer. It goes against all my valued inhibitions. But a bit of me wonders if this is a challenge for me. After all, Jesus healed many sick people who came to him but there were probably plenty who stayed at home, afraid to become a public spectacle. Do I need to humble myself before God and ask for healing in this way?*

5. *There is a deeper concern that God may be dealing with me in this. Fiona and I cope with loads of stuff and are involved in so much at church and beyond. Are we being taught a lesson about trusting in God? I have certainly got to the point when I cannot cope. Fiona has been a great support but perhaps I need to turn*

more directly to God. Is he waiting for that to happen before he heals me? I have not found that my relationship with God has deepened through this crisis. I do not feel close to God. Is there something wrong with the way I am responding to all this?

It has been great to be prayed for by people in church. The Saturday morning prayer time was brilliant. Sarah has such a gift in her prayers that I cried almost as soon as she started. Fiona has experienced the same thing. But I have not put myself in the way of a lot of direct prayer, even within church. I had thought about going to one of the church's special quiet and reflective meetings in May but we were busy one week and I used the excuse of not being able to stifle my cough for an hour the next time. Am I running away from these opportunities?

It was around this time that I started to sense that God was saying it would be a long journey. I felt sure enough of this sense that I shared it with those who prayed with me. To my mind it meant that there would be no quick, miraculous healing. We were in for the long haul, though I had no concept of how long the long haul was and God didn't mention it either. I suppose I might have been hungry for more detail but, looking back, it would not have helped to have known how far away good health would be. In fact, it would have been quite depressing. Instead, God told me what I needed to know. We were going on a journey and he would be with me. A difficult journey is not so daunting when you know you have a guide. So, having got through a bit of an emotional outburst, I set myself to try and be more positive.

FROM:	FIONA MAGGS
DATE:	4 JUNE 2005
TO:	OUR NETWORK OF FRIENDS AND FAMILY
SUBJECT:	THE NEXT STAGE

Just letting you know that we now have an appointment for Solihull Hospital. A letter came telling us that the surgeon wanted to see us in clinic on Wednesday 8th June. Another wait of over a week again. We hope to get the biopsy date when we see him. This was another disappointment for Chris as we had been told that we would probably be able to bypass the clinic stage and just be admitted for the biopsy. Please pray that the date for the biopsy will be very soon after the clinic appointment. We will of course have to wait again for the result! Treatment seems to just get further and further away.

Thanks for all your concern and prayers. We really do appreciate them.

Fiona

JUST VISITING

Over the course of being unwell we have had many visitors to our home, most of whom have brought great encouragement and support. It is interesting though to notice how different these visits have been.

Top of the list for me would be the visits from my two brothers. For some reason they paired up to come and see me, though they live in different parts of the Midlands. It made it a sort of bonding thing I suppose, us men having some difficulty with emotion and the like. It was very noticeable to me how free I felt to talk with my brothers about what was going on and the potential consequences. We talked about death, for example, which had never been on the agenda in other conversations. "What's the worst that can happen?" is a phrase I like. At least if you've considered the worst then anything else is an improvement.

My brothers also took me on little trips. For some reason I had a craving for the seaside. It was too far to travel in my condition but instead we went to St. Nicholas' Park in Warwick for a stroll and bought an ice cream, which was close enough to a seaside experience for me. It was a welcome break from sitting at home and being ill. On another occasion one of them brought some remote control cars that we raced around the house. It was good to just play around instead of talking ill health all the time.

A couple of friends from church, Tim and Alan, were thoughtful enough to spend time playing chess and Scrabble with me. I love board games and become totally absorbed in them. To me it is like the creation of another world, defined by its own rules and little boundaries. And I'm competitive. Perhaps that's why, after Alan had beaten me several times at chess, I suggested we move on to Scrabble. But win or lose it helped those afternoons go by.

Several friends made special trips to come and see us and we appreciated their efforts. Some friends you do not see for a long while but when you meet it is as if no time has passed at all. There is no awkwardness or false politeness, they are kindred spirits and you fall easily into conversation and laughter.

Were there any visits I found unhelpful? No, not really. There were some where the visitors seemed uncomfortable. They were the sort of people who really did not want to impose, so spent much of the time saying they would not stay long, declined a drink and sometimes never even quite sat down. It made their visits seem awkward and rushed and I would have much preferred them to relax and let me be their host for a while. Even so, I appreciated their coming at all.

Having said that some were overly eager to get away, there were a few who were the opposite. They would plonk themselves down on the sofa and settle in, their presence seemingly adequate to bring succour to the sick without the need for much conversation at all. Playing the host could then become a little tiring as the emphasis was on us to entertain them. But once again, we were thankful for their intentions.

One visitor who deserves special mention is a lady who lived in America but was staying with a relative locally for a few months. Her name was Margo. We only met her by chance. Since our own church had no service one Sunday in August we visited the local parish church and Margo was doing the same. The vicar prayed with us afterwards and Margo joined the group when she heard I was unwell. It was kind of her to do so but even more thoughtful to follow up with a visit and then telephone calls from America when she returned there. She had no duty of care through friendship but her actions brought love to us in a very real way.

Just before she left our home she launched into prayer for us. It was a sudden move. She was down on her knees and prayer was upon us before we knew, but it was very welcome.

So thank you to all those who take the time and effort to visit the sick. On behalf of all the sick (if I could be so bold as to assume such a role) let me just say we do appreciate it.

FROM: **FIONA MAGGS**
DATE: **8 JUNE 2005**
TO: **OUR NETWORK OF FRIENDS AND FAMILY**
SUBJECT: **THE NEXT INSTALMENT**

Today we went to see the surgeon at Solihull Hospital. He was very informative and showed us the scan pictures. The tumour is quite large and pressing on a few internal structures. He has explained the procedure that they are going to carry out for the biopsy and what it all entails. Chris is going to be admitted on Sunday for surgery on Monday. They initially gave us a date of 20th June but we both told him that we couldn't wait that long, so eventually we were squeezed in on Monday (he did try and see if there was room on Friday's operating list). He will definitely be in until Tuesday, maybe longer. They may need to put drains in following surgery and then the results may take up to 2 weeks!! They will then refer us onto an Oncologist. We should be at a treatment stage in up to 4 weeks. It looks like there is quite a long road ahead with treatment and hospital visits. The operation is to happen at Heartlands Hospital and we are going in tomorrow afternoon for all the pre-admission tests.

Thank you for continuing to pray for us. Please pray that the biopsy will be straightforward with no complications (including MRSA!). Pray for Chris as he has never been into hospital before and so is a little apprehensive (although he is looking forward to having a good sleep with the general anaesthetic). Pray for me and the children as we manage life! (Tim has his last exam tomorrow).

Thanks again
Fiona

ROOM WITH A VIEW

I was 43 years old and had never stayed overnight in a hospital. My impression as a visitor was that they were places to keep away from. I don't like the smell for a start. It must be all that cleansing agent in one place that gets to me. Then there is the aged appearance of the place. So often they look like something from the fifties, or earlier, built with all the modern conveniences of the time except a maintenance department. And how do they manage to smell clean and still look so grubby? The rambling corridors are designed to disorientate you as soon as you turn a corner and signage uses medical names that mean nothing to anyone but the staff. Car parks are hard to get into, rarely have any spaces left when you do and charge a fortune.

Heartlands fitted my preconceptions all the way. With difficulty parking and the pre-admission department being hidden away in a disused corridor with an armed blockade at the end (I exaggerate, but only just) we ended up arriving late. As usual we had to wait ages in a stuffy little room with a lot of sick people. I tried not to cough over everyone, though the odd cough now and then was fine as it let everyone know I was a genuine case. But when my turn came, the nurse who did the checks – blood pressure, lungs, ECG and some blood tests – was very pleasant and professional. It continues to amaze me how NHS staff keep so cheerful, in front of patients at least, given the state of their working environment.

The day I was due to go in was a Sunday. We had to call the hospital in the morning before church, to check that there was a bed for me. This is a nice little touch, presumably designed to keep patients on edge in the run up to admittance. At church the subject was trust and I found myself reflecting on the fact that so much of the stuff I could have put my trust in – work, health, even active church leadership – had been stripped away. It proved easier to put my trust in God in these unpleasant circumstances than it might have done if all was well.

We got to Ward 4 just after 6 p.m. I had a bed by the window, looking out over a dull squat building, a rarely used road and a couple of refuse disposal units. All the others in our six-bed bay were older men but friendly (if able to talk). Our names were written above our beds and I was pleased to see I was sharing a ward with an institution - Albert Hall.

The chap next to me was in a bad condition and was often bringing back food. He used the bed pan regularly so the curtains got pulled around but the sound effects remained very clear. Then there was a leakage of some sort and the nurses had to change all the bedclothes and his pyjamas. The rest of us made great efforts to appear not to have noticed.

Although I was unwell, in the context of the ward I felt relatively healthy, being able to eat, walk around, and perform my own bodily functions. In fact, I found it hard to feel part of the fraternity until I made the transition into my pyjamas and got under the covers. I resisted putting on the unsightly surgical stockings, preferring to leave that until the morning.

One of the main features of hospital life is the drug round and I found myself anticipating it even on that first night. As an in-patient I was no longer allowed to control my own drug intake and was dependent on the nurse granting my request. It arrived at 11 p.m. and I was allowed a couple of painkillers to get me through the night. They did not help me sleep though. I felt drowsy enough and was both relaxed and comfortable but even so I lay awake for long periods. Hospital wards are not the easiest places to sleep, with people moving around much of the time and drip alarms going off repeatedly. I comforted myself with the thought that tomorrow's anaesthetic would allow me to get some rest.

Things started happening from about 6.30 a.m. on the ward but I was still dozing when a doctor came to see me to discuss the operation and get my consent. He also drew a big arrow on my left side, another nice little personal touch. You can imagine the scenarios that led to this practice – the wrong leg amputated for example, or the surgeon unable to locate the tumour because he's gone in on the wrong side of the chest. Then somebody says, "Hey, let's put a big arrow on the side we're supposed to fix so this won't happen again!" Medical science takes another step forward.

Then my surgeon came to see me and talked about what he was going to do. He said I would only need a drain if they have to puncture the lining of the lung but he hopes to avoid that. I do too.

He told me I was due to go to theatre at midday. It remains one of those strange quirks that the word 'theatre' covers such differing arenas as the operating room and the stage, one portraying the complexities of life and death for entertainment, the other dealing with the real thing. It used to be traditional to dress up to go to the stage theatre, and still is in some quarters. I also dressed for the occasion, putting on a daringly exposing gown along with a pair of heavy, unsightly, white surgical stockings and then settled down for the curtain to rise.

My throat was very dry after not being able to drink all morning but otherwise I felt fine about the process. It would get me closer to the treatment I needed.

They came for me just before 11 a.m. I was wheeled in the bed, propped up and able to see where I was going. We passed through some double doors into part of the hospital closed off to patients normally. Gone were the rows of creaky iron bedsteads containing poorly patients. Gone was the mess and turmoil of day-to-day living. This was theatre-world. Here it was all shiny clean metal and bright lights. This was the unreal world inhabited by surgeons and anaesthetists, who steal a man's consciousness and reduce him to mere flesh and blood. And I was next on their list.

To be fair, the anaesthetists were a lot more human than I've portrayed. The cramped anti-chamber I went into first was filled with five or six of them, all eager to tell me their names and how much they wanted to help me. They ran through a series of questions about crowns, diabetes and allergies and I confirmed my patient number again. Then it was "just a scratch" and a bit of a cold feeling in my arm before I was gone.

FROM: **FIONA MAGGS**
DATE: **13 JUNE 2005**
TO: **OUR NETWORK OF FRIENDS AND FAMILY**
SUBJECT: **BIOPSY DAY**

I have just come back from visiting Chris at Heartlands Hospital and you will be pleased to hear that everything has gone really well. He was sitting up in bed waiting for me when I went. The biopsy went well without any need for any extras (i.e. drains if they needed to cut into the lung or more than one incision - they had said they might need to approach the tumour from more than one angle). This is the result of all that prayer I am sure.

He should be able to come out tomorrow if he is still OK in the morning. He may need a few checks like a chest x-ray and hopefully will not feel too bad when the pain relief wears off.

Thanks again to everyone for your prayers. We will hopefully find out next week what the results of the biopsy are and what the next steps are going to be.

Fiona

THE WAITING GAME

With everything going well in terms of recovery I was glad to be told that I could leave hospital the day after the operation. It had not been a bad experience but even so, I wanted to get home. In the old days patients would spend a week or so recuperating after such an operation but I was happy to live in the era when they wanted the beds back as soon as possible.

Even so, there are certain hurdles to cross before being discharged. First I needed an X-ray, which involved finding a porter and a wheelchair and then waiting in the X-ray department for quite a while. Then a doctor needed to be found with the time to glance at the X-ray and confirm everything was where it should be. This is no easy feat. The glancing bit is straightforward but finding a doctor is not. They have their ward rounds of course, during which they congregate in large gangs, but after that it seems they disperse to all corners of the hospital, beckoned by beepers to deal with a series of emergencies, all of which are apparently more critical than my X-ray. Eventually one had a couple of minutes to spare and gave me the green light.

There was still a final hurdle in the form of dispensing tablets. The hospital sends you off with a little party bag of drugs to keep you going for a week or so. In my case this was a heady mix of painkillers and laxatives. These were signed off by the doctor and then the prescription was sent to pharmacy, where life must be very busy. It would be several hours before my little package was ready and I could finally leave.

Unfortunately, my bed was needed for someone else and I was asked to decant to the Discharge Lounge. In fact, my departure from the ward was a little rushed in that a porter and wheelchair arrived at the same time as they told me I needed to be transferred. Fiona had taken my overnight bag home when I arrived and was bringing it back to pick me up later. So all my worldly possessions were bundled into a couple of plastic bags marked "Patient Property" and I was wheeled off, clutching them to myself like a down-and-out evicted from a squat.

Though the Discharge Lounge at the Alexandra Hospital had been no more than a waiting room, it would have featured much higher in the rankings than its namesake at Heartlands. The facilities were no more than a square of cheap plastic chairs and the obligatory daytime TV. There was a cup of tea shortly after arrival but having just missed lunch on the ward there was nothing else to eat or drink for the four hours I sat there. On the positive side, there were no property development programmes and I did get to watch two shows I cannot imagine I would have sat through under any other circumstances.

One was 'Date my Daughter', which, if I remember it right, featured three mums, each spending time with a young lad in order to persuade him to date their respective daughters. At the end, the lad had to choose a date based on his time with the mothers. A few things strike me as odd here. First, why are the mums so desperate to get their daughters a boyfriend? I thought parents were supposed to be protective about their little darlings. Second, what self-respecting daughter would want her mum involved in the process these days anyway? And third, the whole programme seems to be based on the principle that all girls turn out like their mums. Even if it's true, it really is too depressing a prospect for day time viewing.

Then there was 'Cash Cab', in which unsuspecting members of the public found that stepping into a London cab had catapulted them into the realms of low-budget TV. In order to win money and get to their chosen London destination, they had to answer general knowledge questions. Fine, I suppose. But the trouble was that if you got a certain number of questions wrong you were turfed out of the cab and abandoned somewhere en route. Amazingly, none of the losers seemed daunted by this prospect and took it well if they lost. For myself, finding travel around London fairly daunting and usually being late for a meeting, I find the concept horrifying and will always peer suspiciously into cabs before entering them from now on.

Meanwhile, back in the Discharge Lounge I was not the only one waiting. A couple of people were there before me and one of them was still there when I left. They were waiting not only for tablets but also hospital transport to go back home. There is no doubt that free hospital transport is a wonderful facility to have available but there is a price to pay in terms of the proportion of your life spent waiting for it.

Nevertheless, complaining about the wait gave us some common ground and helped create a community feeling. Typically British, we stuck it out with good humour, just like stories of the war. I wonder whether the same stoic attitude will continue in younger generations. There is always a tendency to think not but I have a theory that this British attitude is essentially a result of our changeable weather and will persist with us as long as the rain continues to fall.

So it was back home for more waiting, this time for the results of the biopsy. We had been told it would be next week but we were beginning to learn that a week in medicine is a long time, and so it proved to be.

FROM:	**FIONA MAGGS**
DATE:	**23 JUNE 2005**
TO:	**OUR NETWORK OF FRIENDS AND FAMILY**
SUBJECT:	**CLINIC DATE**

Just to let you all know that we now have a date to go to clinic to get the results of the biopsy. This is not as soon as we would have liked. The clinic is next Thursday (30th June) at 8.45am. At least we will be at the front of the queue to be seen.

Fiona

A PAIN IN THE ......

One of the side effects of the operation process is constipation and I am not one to let such an opportunity go by without comment. Any excuse to talk about my bowel movements and I'm off. Fiona says I worry too much but the fact is I'm very attached to my bowels and I did say I would be as honest as I could. So anyone of a nervous disposition may prefer to bypass this section all together.

I had been somewhat irregular even before going into hospital but the effect of the anaesthetic and scores of painkiller tablets was severe congestion. Laxative tablets were automatically available at the hospital to counteract this but nothing moved while I was there and things did not improve once back home. I became obsessed with the issue, as these extracts from my personal diary reveal.

Wednesday 15 June	No bowel movements today and no sign of anything happening. Fiona tells me not to worry but when she's not looking I do!
Thursday 16 June	Have decided to cut down on the painkillers in the hope that it will relieve the constipation. Missed one dose this evening but took the usual overnight ones.
Friday 17 June	Attempted to evacuate the bowels this morning but after considerable straining and grunting remained unsuccessful. Did not feel like any lunch because of the discomfort and was quite desperate at the thought of having to go through it all again. Managed to deliver the goods early afternoon but it left me with a pain in my bottom, which particularly hurts when I cough. I seem to cough quite frequently still!
Saturday 18 June	The bottom pain has not eased and I am nervous of going to the toilet until it does.
Sunday 19 June	Managed a movement today, which was not as painful as Friday's but there was a

	fair amount of blood this time and the pain continues when coughing.
Monday 20 June	My bottom continues to be sore, making sitting into an art form and hurting whenever I cough.
Tuesday 21 June	Another bowel movement this morning – still very strenuous and painful, with more fresh blood. I book an appointment at the GP's on Thursday in the hope they can identify the problem. I am preoccupied with my bowels and the anticipated pain, although there is less pain when I cough at the moment.

Now I know it isn't the sort of subject we like to talk about and, in the context of prayer, I never would have asked for laying on of hands but the reality is that constipation was probably the most physically painful experience of the whole journey. The toilet is, quite rightly, a solitary environment. When your digestive system is doing all it can to try and shift concrete, your body is racked with waves of pain, hot sweats are breaking out and there is no end in sight, it is a lonely place to be. I am not exaggerating when I say that at times I felt like I was going to die.

Of course, the ladies are all thinking, "You should try having a baby!" You may be right, but this is the closest I am likely to come and at least I can feel a little more empathy for you. On the other hand, your end product is worth waiting for, whereas mine, when it eventually comes, raises no more than a brief smile of (literal) relief before being flushed away.

On Thursday 23 June I had an appointment with the GP. I am sure it says reams about my character that before going I wrote out details of my bowel movements, laxatives and painkillers over the course of June in a comprehensive table. A very absorbing document, I thought, and the doctor was kind enough to read it with apparent interest. After a brief examination he confirmed I had piles. He gave me tablets to encourage daily bowel movements, a solution to soften the material and a suppository to loosen things up down below.

This was my first experience of suppositories and I'm afraid I never really got the hang of it. The instructions seemed fairly straightforward but the practice less so. Positioning is everything, and a relaxed attitude, but I failed on both scores and much of what I achieved in terms of penetration was reversed when I stood up again. I remain convinced that that particular orifice should be used in a one-way direction only.

On a more serious note, problems like constipation, and other pains and discomforts to do with the more personal areas, are not always easy to talk about. I know I was very reluctant to mention it, even when people asked if there were particular areas of concern. When I did, it was reassuring to have the sympathy of others who had had similar problems and understood the experience. Even so, I found myself mentioning this particular issue with an embarrassed smirk, as if it was more of a confession than a sharing of information.

I am not about to suggest that we should make a push (no pun intended) to get constipation out in the open, though I think if we did it would be surprising how much pain and suffering people are bearing without feeling able to tell anyone. No, each person will have their own limits of endurance and levels of inhibition and only when those thresholds are breached will they want to share such problems with others.

Enough on this subject for now. For those with the stomach, take heart that we will return to it later on.

FROM:	**FIONA MAGGS**
DATE:	**24 JUNE 2005**
TO:	**OUR NETWORK OF FRIENDS AND FAMILY**
SUBJECT:	**AN ANSWER TO PRAYER**

Having let you all know yesterday that we have an appointment we were surprised to receive another letter in the post today. This was an appointment for Monday afternoon to see the Respiratory Consultant at the Alexandra Hospital (our original doctor). Having phoned to find out if this was correct we have discovered that he has spoken to the surgeon (at Heartlands Hospital) and has the results and will discuss them with us on Monday afternoon at 3.00pm. We will also see the surgeon on Thursday. Having felt like we had ages to wait, it now feels very close.

I will let you all know what happens next week as we do hope that we will now be able to find out what the treatment is going to be and an idea of how long it may all take.

Thank you for continuing to pray for us all.

Fiona

WORDS OF WISDOM

On the subject of sharing news, things are very different once you have a serious health issue. In normal circumstances people ask how you are as a routine greeting and my stock response before I was ill was, "Fine thanks, and you?"

immediately diverting the attention away from me. For a long while I found myself repeating the stock response automatically and then having to stop myself because the person was asking about progress with my illness and had a genuine concern.

Throughout my ill health, I never felt I got very good at answering the "How are you?" question. All the time I was trying to judge the level of reply they were looking for. Did they want the twenty-second version or the five-minute one or the 'I'll put the kettle on' epic? I fear I may have put a good few people through the longer version, particularly as the illness progressed and I got more used to talking about myself. It became the automatic subject of all my conversations and I must have been a bit of a bore at times.

It was not only the length of the conversations that changed though. I also found a lot more people were happy to skip the superficial conversation and get straight to the bigger issue. This was most evident in people who had been praying for me because they had heard of my situation through friends or family, though they did not know me themselves. I would meet such people periodically and they would feel an immediate bond, enabling them to say things like, "Ah, you're the one with the cancer", which would seem an unlikely way to start a conversation with a stranger in other circumstances. I have no complaints about such introductions. The prayers of those I do not know personally have been a great benefit and express their love very eloquently. I thank God for them. It's just that having so many people know a lot about you takes a bit of getting used to. It's like being a celebrity but for all the wrong reasons.

As part of a Christian community, through my church and wider connections, there was also some pressure to draw closer to God through suffering, while growing in wisdom and holiness; at least, I felt so. To be honest the pressure was probably self-induced but there were times when conversations seemed to lead towards the question, "What deep spiritual truths have you learned through this experience?" and I felt rather inadequate to answer. Sometimes I would attempt to draw a conclusion together and put it into words. On one occasion when I did so, the two people I was speaking to went very quiet and gazed down at the floor. I was not sure what this signified until one of them murmured sincerely, "Very profound". I joined them in their moment of contemplation, thinking, "What did I say?"

Perhaps because of this sense that I ought to have something to say, I put together a letter for all those within the Christian community who were following my progress. If it sounds a bit pious I can only apologise. The sentiment is genuine. We sent it out on the 25th of June.

Dear friends and family

Sorry to send you a general letter rather than individual replies but there are so many of you who have sent cards or called or shown us support over the last few weeks that it would be impossible to respond any other way. This letter is particularly written to you as brothers and sisters in the body of Jesus Christ because I want you to know that your support and prayers have not been in vain. I know that many of you have passed on details of my circumstances to other Christians and the network of prayer is incredibly wide. It is humbling to think that there are people across the UK and in America too, many of whom I do not know, who are lifting us up in prayer. Please pass on this message to them as well so that we can thank them.

As most of you know, we have an appointment soon to discuss the results of the surgical biopsy. It seems incredible that it has taken two months from the first chest X-ray on 26 April to get to the point of diagnosis. Naturally we are keen to move on to the next stage and get some treatment started soon and we have been frustrated at various points over the last two months as each set of tests has failed to identify the problem and more intrusive tests have been necessary. On one occasion I remember saying to Fiona, "What's the point of having all these people praying for me if this happens?" Sorry if that destroys anybody's impression of me as being super-spiritual. It was a low point and I am not proud of my ingratitude. But the last few weeks have made me think about prayer and its purpose quite a lot.

As I said earlier, it has been wonderful to receive messages of support and prayer from so many people. I really enjoy going to church on Sunday morning because so many people there want to encourage me and it is good to be prayed for. However, I have been making the mistake in my mind of seeing this as the support of people rather than God. Somehow I had been looking for God elsewhere. I was looking for God in the miraculous, and that had not come. Recently I have come to realise that God is in it all. It is his body, the body of Jesus Christ, people like you, who have been there for us and so God has expressed his compassion and care through you. God has written his thoughts on cards that you sent. God has spoken his encouragement through your mouth. God has been there in practical ways through your actions.

So I thank you and I thank God and I ask you to continue to pray for us as we get results and go on to the treatment stage. I am very open to God doing something miraculous but if he does then it must be in his own time. Or he may choose not to. My prayer is this; that I walk the path that God decides is right for this journey – wherever that may take me. He is good and I choose to put my trust in him.

May God bless you in your journey with him,

Love from Chris Maggs

I know my father liked the letter. Every time I spoke to him for weeks afterwards he mentioned another group of people he'd sent it to, or read it to, all of whom (according to his account) thought it was wonderful. Well, I am glad to have brought a warm smile to his face at least.

FROM:	**FIONA MAGGS**
DATE:	**27 JUNE 2005**
TO:	**OUR NETWORK OF FRIENDS AND FAMILY**
SUBJECT:	**MONDAY'S NEWS**

Another hospital visit. Another long wait to be seen. This time we were prepared for a wait so were quite relaxed. We are feeling like old hands at this clinic business. We smiled to ourselves as those new to the clinic were not quite sure of the routine.

The news for Chris is that they are still unable to identify the tumour. It does seem that it is rare and they still have no idea. The plan however is to try and remove it. The tumour will then be looked at to try and identify it and a decision as to whether it is benign or malignant will be made and any further treatment decided on. At the moment the doctors have not been able to find any signs of malignancy but that does not rule it out yet. We are seeing the surgeon on Thursday morning but the doctors (respiratory and thoracic surgeon) are meeting on Wednesday and if they change their plan they will let us know. When the surgery can be done and how much of the tumour they are going to be able to remove will hopefully become clear. There are risks involved as the phrenic nerve is very close (goes to the diaphragm). We are now hoping that surgery will happen in the next few weeks and then it will be another wait for more histology results as they take a look at the tumour. Chris is just keen to get rid of the tumour and relieve his symptoms as quickly as possible.

We await our appointment on Thursday to get some dates and a clearer idea of what the surgery will involve. Thank you for praying for us.

Fiona

WEATHERING THE STORM

The news that the results of the biopsy were inconclusive was obviously a disappointment because it meant more weeks of coughing, breathlessness and lack of sleep. At this point I was frequently coughing to the point of being sick. Unpleasant as this was, throwing up at least brought some temporary relief. It was obvious I was getting worse and the prospect of any treatment remained some distance away. Until a clear diagnosis could be found there was nothing they could do.

Despite the situation we remained calm. Fiona had been saying on the previous Sunday how much she felt at peace. For us, knowing God is in control is the only source of such a feeling. It does not mean that we expect him to put everything right, or rearrange the natural order of things simply to suit us, but we know that someone with such power is watching over us. It is a difficult concept to explain when you try and put it into words. Maybe it is like watching a film where you know that everything will work out alright in the end, even though you can see more trouble ahead. But when I say "work out alright" I do not mean that I think I know the ending, or even what "alright" means. I simply trust the judgement of the one who is doing the directing. To be blunt, cancer can kill people, and I am not exempt, but from a Christian perspective that would not be the ending, simply a continuation of the journey.

As I am writing this passage, over a year after the event, I am in the process of reading "The Problem of Pain" by C S Lewis. It is a book I read once before, many years ago but if anyone had asked me, I could not have recalled its content. Yet as I read it again now I discover with pleasure that his ideas must have sunk deep into my understanding as he puts into words far more eloquently than I ever could the underlying reasons for suffering in a world created by a loving God. He expresses ideas and concepts in ways that help me to understand my own often muddled thoughts and I find myself grateful to him both for this and for putting those thoughts there in the first place. I will not do him the injustice of attempting a summary here but would recommend the book to anyone.

This understanding of God and our relationship to him has served me well in the face of suffering and proved itself more than just a nice theory. And so it should be. Any theory that falls apart in the storm is not worth clinging to the wreckage of. One that holds firm has proved itself worthy. So I should not, perhaps, be so surprised that I have little to offer by way of new revelations through this experience. Instead, my faith in God and my understanding of him has altered little and I simply have a firmer conviction that Jesus is the way, the truth and the life. If I say that I have stood the test I do not mean that I believe God has specifically selected me to have cancer. I just mean that in a world where suffering exists for all, I have weathered this particular storm. Other storms will come and perhaps be stronger tests still. I pray for the courage to hold on to the one who I believe will bring me out on the other side.

It would be wrong of me to concentrate entirely on getting through to the other side of troubles, as if God were waiting at the finish line with a bunch of flowers and a gold medal. There have been times when I believe I have seen God at work in the process, though often in such subtle ways that I only catch a glimpse and am left wondering.

The day we got the news that the biopsy was inconclusive, Fiona made a few telephone calls as well as sending around an email. Afterwards she happened to mention that she was disappointed not to have heard anything over the last two months from a couple of people she would have expected to have been in touch. We got calls from both of them in the next two days! It seemed to us that God had been listening to our conversation and given them both a nudge. It was an encouragement to hear from them anyway, but an added bonus to sense God at work. A similar 'coincidence' happened again a few months later and Fiona is now more cautious about what she says!

FROM: **FIONA MAGGS**
DATE: **30 JUNE 2005**
TO: **OUR NETWORK OF FRIENDS AND FAMILY**
SUBJECT: **GETTING CLOSER!**

This morning we went to see the surgeon who did Chris' biopsy and find out what they are planning for the next stage. As we found out on Monday they have now decided to operate and try to remove the tumour. As they still do not know what type of tumour it is they will be doing some tests while Chris is on the operating table and how much they take away will depend on whether it is malignant or benign. It is going to be about a 4 hour operation as it is going to be tricky to remove. It is attached to the nerve that goes to his voice box and also sitting on the major vessels that come out of his heart. It is probable that they are going to have to cut through the nerve and that will result in some further problems in the future. The lungs are not involved at all apparently. His cough is due to the voice box nerve being irritated.

They had given us a date of 12th July although the surgeon was trying to see if he could do the operation sooner privately. However, this afternoon we got a phone call saying that they had a cancellation and Chris could go in this Monday to have the operation on Tuesday (5th July). It is going to be quite a big operation and they will be opening him up right down his front. He will be wired back together and that will take about 12 weeks to heal. If they do decide to do radiotherapy that can happen after 6 weeks.

I think that that is a brief account of what is going on at the moment. Chris is obviously quite anxious about being opened up and having his breast bone sawn in half! Please can I ask for you to continue praying for us. Tim has gone away on his silver Duke of Edinburgh expedition today and will not be back until Monday afternoon/evening so may not

get to see his dad. (He does know he is having the op, but not when.)
Hannah has taken her first piano exam this afternoon and Luke is just
getting on with life. I am sure that God will be with us through all that
happens. This week we were made aware of his presence as I made a
comment about something and we had two phone calls very shortly after
related to what I had said! God was listening!!!

Thank you once again.

Fiona

PICKING UP THE PIECES

I've never had a problem with relaxing. I can do it for
hours. I'd like to claim that I'm genetically lazy but it is not a
habit I've noticed in my family. Perhaps I'm just gifted. Having
said that, relaxing for me does usually involve doing something.
Obviously it has to be something other than work, otherwise it
would not be relaxing. As far as I'm concerned, anything in the
DIY or gardening areas are firmly in the work category. Relaxing
includes reading, playing games, doing puzzles and, of course,
watching TV. I found that I had plenty of time for these activities
now that I was not at work and my health prevented me from
doing anything practical.

The main activity that occupied me at this time was jigsaw
puzzles. Normally I rarely do them simply because they take too
long. The dining room table can be occupied for months to
complete a 1000 piece puzzle and the best part of a year when I
have attempted our one and only Connoisseur 2000 piece jigsaw
of Cockington Forge, Devon. With the extra time available it
seemed an ideal opportunity to get the job done. And perversely,

that is largely my motivation – getting the job done. I have completed a number of psychological tests over the years, trying to pin me down to type, and have discovered, among other things, that I am a completer-finisher. I am compelled by a desire to finish things off. So, for example, if there is a choice of things to eat for lunch, my inclination is to finish something off rather than choose what I like best. I would rather watch a video of something I've recorded earlier than watch a programme that's on now. Books have to be read to the end even if I'm not enjoying them and letters opened have to be dealt with rather than stuffed back in the envelope and left on the table. It is in my make up that such acts help to make the world a better place to live.

Jigsaw puzzles are similarly regarded as a job that needs completing. Someone has, rather thoughtlessly, left it in pieces and it needs to be sorted. So once started I will spend hours pointlessly poring over oddly shaped tiny bits of cardboard, to the exclusion of all around me, simply because it needs to be done. And it has the added advantage that every piece fitted is a step closer, so I can feel I am making progress every time another one slots into place. Not that I am sentimental about the finished product. Once completed I have no qualms about breaking it up, putting it back in its box and returning it to its shelf. After all, the clearing away is another job done.

Crosswords have a similar claim on my priorities. I hate to leave one unfinished. The same principle applies at Christmas when I have accumulated a range of seasonal confectionary. Only one pack will be opened at a time and its contents gradually consumed, the pleasure partly in the taste but also in getting the job done. Only then can the seal on the next be breached.

You might think that this approach would naturally lead to a tidy life. In some areas it does but certainly not in all. My desks, for example, both at home and at work, are generally covered with piles of papers. This is because life, being what it is, does not lend itself to finishing jobs off. There are always reasons why things cannot be completed yet; waiting for someone else to do their part, or a date to arrive, or a decision to be made. So unfinished jobs pile up. Tidy people put the paperwork away until it is needed but as a completer-finisher I cannot put it away until it is done. I like to keep it there, ready for action.

I would hate you to think that I am obsessive in these traits. It is easy to pick out the things that make me appear so but there are probably others that create more of a balance. Why, for example, do I not have the same desire to finish off those gardening and DIY jobs? The gardening I can account for. It always seems depressing to me that plants, and particularly those plants we designate weeds, will grow back within weeks. It is impossible to 'finish off' the garden and so I lose the heart to tackle it at all.

I cannot make the same claim for DIY though. Instead I fall back to my original premise that I am naturally lazy. The fact that poor health prevents me from doing the jobs I dislike and gives time to do the things I enjoy proves that every cloud has a silver lining after all.

FROM: FIONA MAGGS
DATE: 4 JULY 2005
TO: OUR NETWORK OF FRIENDS AND FAMILY
SUBJECT: JUST SO YOU KNOW

Chris is happily established on Ward 4 at the Heartlands hospital. He is first on the list for surgery tomorrow which should start just before 9.00am. He will then be moved to HDU (High Dependency Unit).

We now just wait for tomorrow and all that that entails. Thank you for all your concerns and prayers.

Fiona

FLY ON THE WALL

I am trying to recall my frame of mind as I went into hospital for surgery. My diary gives me a few hints. For example, an entry on 1 July said, "It seems possible that in a month or so I could be able to go back to work". Hah! Little did I know at the time. Even if the operation had been all the treatment that was needed, and I obviously thought that was a possibility, there is no way I would have recovered sufficiently within a month to return to work. But this shows quite well my lack of understanding of what was about to happen. I don't like staying in hospitals but I had confidence in the staff and knew that it was all being done for the best. So I looked forward to the long-term benefit of getting better and did not think much about what they were actually going to do.

Fiona was just the opposite. From the start she was keen to understand all the possibilities and know all the details. The internet provides a wealth of information and she would happily spend hours investigating different maladies and the experiences of those who had gone through them. She probably found my lack of interest disappointing but I took the view that knowing what might happen and what subsequent treatment there might be would only add to my distress, not alleviate it. Whatever would be, would be.

On 3 July I wrote, "I feel apprehensive in some ways because this is major surgery but it is the only way to get better and I am glad to be getting on with it". And on 4 July I commented that I was looking forward to the period after surgery when the effects of the anaesthetic would, at least for a while, leave me with no pain and a restful feeling.

As before, I was put on a six-bed male bay in Ward 4. Opposite was a man who had just had an operation. He was in agony; hardly an encouraging sign. Next to him was a man whose operation, due that day, had been postponed at the last minute due to the identification of an irregular heartbeat. He was grumpy, claiming that he was fine and they should have gone ahead. It must be strange to be told you are too unwell to be treated, and disheartening if, like me, you can feel yourself getting worse. Another older man was lying in bed hardly conscious, apparently too ill for his operation as well. He had been like this for some time and, unlike Mr Grumpy, did not look too long for this world.

In every bay, it seems, there are a couple of people who get on really well and chat all the time. This was the bloke next to me and beyond him an Irishman who was also the bay jester. Their merry banter either lifted the spirits or got on your nerves, depending on whether you wanted to sleep or not.

I am not a great one for conversation. I don't mind chatting in the right social setting but at the same time I'm quite content to be quiet if I can, and simply observe. A hospital ward is not my idea of the right social setting for anything and I do not like the fact that talking from bed to bed means that everyone can hear what you say. Not that I was saying anything secret. I just didn't think other people should be burdened with my banal conversation. But privacy was in short supply here, as illustrated by the evening drug rounds when the nurse would call loudly across the bay, "Anything for your bowels Mr Maggs?"

So I did not join in the conversation much and felt a bit antisocial. There had been a few comments from Christian friends that my time in hospital would be a good witnessing opportunity. I am afraid I did not embrace the moment. It seemed no easier bringing God into the conversation here than anywhere else and, anyway, I preferred to stay under cover. If someone asked, of course, I would not deny my faith but I convinced myself that the best thing was to fit in and be normal.

My cover was blown at 6 a.m. the next morning when I was aroused from my stupor by a nurse shouting to me from some distance, "Mr Maggs, do you go to church?" For a moment I wondered whether my quiet saintly behaviour had led to some inner conviction in the lady and hence to her appeal to know the source of my inner peace. Alas, not. She had simply been on a nursing study day yesterday and met a friend of mine from church. So everyone knew I was a Christian after that. It might have been a launching pad from which to preach the gospel but I admit my mind was elsewhere as I donned the operating gown and those surgical stockings. I don't think I was worried about dying on the operating table at the time but looking back I would hate to have met my maker in that outfit!

The previous night had been difficult, as expected in a hospital bed. I was up and down six times to the toilet before 2.30 a.m. and hardly slept during that period. Although I felt drowsy and was lying in bed comfortably, my mind would not switch off; it kept running over all sorts of things unrelated to the operation, most of which made little sense in the more lucid moments.

One of the doctors had come to see me the previous evening to explain what they were doing, then in the morning a nurse arrived followed by an anaesthetist. Next was another doctor, who wanted a blood sample as there was a problem with the one they had. This delayed the operation for a couple of hours but by mid-morning I was wheeled back to theatre-world and taken into a dreamless sleep by those lovely anaesthetist people.

My skin was cut open, my chest bone sawn in two, my ribs shifted out of the way, my heart laid bare, my lungs deflated and the tumour exposed to the surgeon's knife. I'm not a fan of those fly-on-the-wall medical programmes that follow people through their hospital treatment but if I had to watch part of such a programme I'd choose the operations. There is something quite wonderful about seeing the inside of a human body, especially one still alive. Those essential organs we learn about from an early age and live with all our lives are revealed for what they are. They are not the neat illustrations in biology textbooks or the smooth hard plastic objects of a 3-D model but weird-shaped colourful slimy bits of tissue that would be damp and spongy to touch and gross to smell. The reality is an awesome mess and you wonder how the surgeons can ever find anything in there, let alone fix it. I would love to have a video of my operation and see myself for what I really am. Perhaps it could be a new source of NHS income, with copies to buy for relatives and friends as well.

One thing I particularly would have liked to see was what my tumour looked like. Since being told I had one my mind had tried to picture it. What was its shape? How long? Where did it lie exactly? What colour was it? I did try asking once but the consultant smiled at me as if I was joking and the moment passed. But it was a serious question. To me my tumour remained a difficult thing to battle against unless I could visualise it. I did see its dark image on the x-rays and scan pictures but it did not help me much. I only knew for sure it was there because of the poor health I was suffering. It must be harder still for those who are told they have a tumour and yet suffer no ill-effects. I never got very far in developing a mental picture. A glimpse of it in the operating room nestled in amongst the blood and gore would have been fascinating; the tumour as a concept revealed at last in the flesh.

There was no TV crew and no fly-on-the-wall documentary. When I think about it, perhaps it is for the best. An operating theatre with a fly on the wall would probably have hygiene issues.

FROM:	**FIONA MAGGS**
DATE:	**5 JULY 2005**
TO:	**OUR NETWORK OF FRIENDS AND FAMILY**
SUBJECT:	**OPERATION DAY**

Here I am again!

Well, the operation has been done although I do not know at the moment what was done. The only thing I have found out so far is that they had to cut into the lining of the heart. His heart is not very happy at the moment consequently. It seemed better not to try and get answers to questions tonight as Chris is not well enough to take anything in at the moment. He was able to talk to me a little, although occasionally asked things like, "Am I meant to be doing something?" and "Should I be doing a report?". He has drips and tubes coming out of most places and they have him on a morphine syringe driver. He has had to have some blood and is now on various fluids and oxygen. He will stay in HDU for around 24 hours and then move back into the ward if he is OK. I shall be back to see him tomorrow afternoon.

Thank you for all your prayer today. I really did feel the benefit of it and felt quite calm and peaceful all day. I also slept really well last night. Please continue to pray for Chris as he has some recovering to do.

Fiona

SORTING OUT THE PLUMBING

I remember very little about the rest of the day of the operation, the morphine and anaesthetic doing a good job, but I do recall the comment in the email about asking if I had to do a report. The initial recovery period was not a peaceful time. My head was buzzing with confused and fretful ideas. I could not make sense of anything and was constantly worried that I was supposed to be doing something. Hence the report I suppose.

If I were a fireman I would probably have asked if there was a fire I needed to attend to. If I were a gardener I'd have been worried about the plants. As an actuary, spending all my life shuffling paper, I thought I should probably be writing it all up. At the time I put this effect down to the morphine but, as it turns out, it is exactly what I am doing now.

As I became a little more aware I discovered I had developed a more extensive plumbing system. Below the long central scar down my chest there were three drains stitched in place in my abdomen; clear plastic tubes just less than a centimetre in diameter to take fluid away from the area around my lungs. They drained into clear plastic bags so I could see the putrid yellow-red liquid oozing out. Both arms and my neck had needles inserted and drips were set up to administer various drugs. And there was the catheter.

This was a contraption I would have dreaded in other circumstances but given how I felt, the practicality of not having to worry about urinating was wonderful. Having said that, I remained more nervous of this particular tube than any other, particularly the possibility of it being accidentally yanked out. As a result I took great care when I or anything around me moved. If I had understood the mechanics better I would have worried less. Apparently the tube is held in place by the end in the bladder being blown up like a balloon. So even a good tug would not have dislodged it. Fortunately, this was never put to the test.

With all of this and an oxygen mask I must have looked a sorry specimen when Fiona came to visit that first evening. It is remarkable what the body can endure though. I was sitting up and eating within 24 hours of the operation and took my first tentative walk shortly afterwards, encumbered with drains and drips on both sides.

My chest was very painful when I coughed, for obvious reasons. I was given a device that allowed me to control my own dose of morphine. A blast was administered every time I pressed the button. Unfortunately it did little to help as my cough would come without warning, followed by the pain. By the time I then pressed the button and felt the benefit, the worst of the pain had passed. And I was finding the effects of the morphine unpleasant anyway. It brought back that fretful feeling and made me confused and agitated. So I weaned myself off it as soon as I could. I preferred to have my head back in working order, despite the pain.

Two days after the operation they decided it was time to remove some of my tubes. I looked forward to this as I was beginning to become more mobile and trailing so much medical equipment around made me feel like some sort of android. I might have been less keen if I had known more about the disengagement process.

The removal of the drain tubes seemed surprisingly basic. First the stitches holding the tubes in place were released. Then I was simply told to take a deep breath and hold it while they pulled out the length of tubing inside me and quickly did up the stitch again to close the hole. The two tubes removed, which the nurse showed me afterwards, were each half a metre in length. There was no local anaesthetic but thankfully the sensation and pain were fairly brief.

I was more nervous when it came to removing the catheter, especially as the student nurse doing so had never done it before. She had asked the senior nurse eagerly if she could "have a go" and I was asked if I minded. Being well brought up, I found myself assuring her that it was fine before I'd really thought about it. Fortunately, it was painless and straightforward; though, as those who have shared the experience will know, not without sensation. The muscles that control water flow had obviously adapted to the presence of the tube and its sudden removal created the overwhelming feeling that I was about to wet the bed. The natural reaction was, of course, to try and control the flow using those same muscles but they did not respond as expected and the sensation continued for some time, though nothing actually escaped.

And then there was the opposite problem; that of persuading those same confused muscles to stop panicking and let me perform. This was not an immediate requirement, the bladder being empty initially because of the catheter, but the nurses were keen that normal service should be resumed as soon as possible. In order to provide them with evidence to this effect required use of a bottle; another new adventure for me. It sounded simple enough but I've never been good at practical things and this proved no exception.

I tried while sitting up in bed and then, with the curtains drawn around, while sitting on the side of the bed, but four decades of holding on, habitually practiced since toilet training, are not easily overcome and I simply could not come up with the goods. It didn't help that I felt a bit of a fool casually sitting there trying to act natural while literally nothing happened. In the end I had to shuffle my way, with my remaining drain in tow, to the men's room and adopt the usual posture before my muscles could be persuaded to relax.

So began the process of becoming human again after the operation; first the return of consciousness, then struggling to reclaim control of my thoughts, shedding much of the plumbing and re-establishing bladder control. However, there was still much work to be done to gain strength and independence. Walking was slow and awkward and my breathing was very shallow. Nausea was never far away and deep sleep on that noisy hospital ward a distant dream.

My parents visited the day after the operation and friends from church the next day. They got little sense out of me and were perhaps surprised at my sorry condition. But each step was a step in the right direction and relative to peers in adjacent beds I was progressing well.

The following day the last drain was removed. This was a different nurse, who seemed to be more motivated by efficiency than compassion. What she lacked in bedside manner she made up for in brute strength and her final closing of the stitch was done with military precision. I suspect she practiced by fastening her army boots.

Now that I was free of tubes I attempted a bath. The equipment was basic and the water was tepid but it felt good to achieve this simple task. The scars from my two operations stood out proudly on my skinny body, like battle wounds bravely won. My days as a topless male model were over before they had even begun.

FROM:	**FIONA MAGGS**
DATE:	**7 JULY 2005**
TO:	**OUR NETWORK OF FRIENDS AND FAMILY**
SUBJECT:	**KEEPING YOU UP TO DATE**

Thought I had just better bring you all up to date on what has happened with Chris over the last couple of days.

He was moved off HDU this afternoon and has had a couple of chest drains, drips, his catheter and his central line (not a tube as in London but tubes going into his neck through which they were giving drugs) removed. He has done a couple of walks with the physio (+ one with just me!). Unfortunately this afternoon he was sick and is feeling really light headed. It may be the morphine (which he has not had any of since this morning as he was feeling so out of it) making him feel so bad.

The news from the operation is not so good. The tumour is definitely malignant and they were unable to remove all of it. That is because it has grown around some major vessels in his chest i.e. aorta + pulmonary vein and others. The tumour had already damaged the left phrenic nerve (the one to his diaphragm) so that side is no longer working. The tumour had also grown into the left lung and they were unable to remove that bit. The result of this is that he will be having further treatment but what and when is still to be arranged.

It seems we still have a long way to go and an awful lot of trusting to do! As we get over one hurdle there seems to be another one ready to attempt. We need to pray that Chris will get over this surgery and that he can get strong enough to cope with the chemotherapy and/or radiotherapy in the next weeks.

Thanks yet again for all your prayers and best wishes. It really is incredible the number of people who are praying and following our progress.

I now need a really good night's sleep!

Fiona

In sickness and in health

It is not even clear to me when the question was first asked. At the end of April a shadow on the lung did not necessarily mean cancer and even in May there remained some doubt as to whether it was a tumour or not. So when did the question, "Is it malignant or benign?" first start to be formed? I suspect that it probably took shape at the back of our minds at the beginning of everything but only got put into words as the evidence mounted. The needle biopsy failed to answer the question and so did the surgical biopsy. It was only by opening me up and slicing off a large section that it was confirmed. "Yes Mr Maggs, your tumour is malignant."

Even after all this experience, I struggle with understanding the medical bits and as I write have to ask Fiona what malignant actually means. In layman's terms it means it has the potential to spread elsewhere and will kill its host if left unchecked. A benign tumour keeps itself to itself. It can do a lot of damage pushing other things out of the way but it is not invasive, whereas a malignant tumour can attack the cells of other organs and grow into them. A malignant tumour might spread through the blood system or the lymphatic system to other areas of the body too.

I notice I referred to the tumour's 'host' just now, as if the tumour were a separate entity, some sort of parasite. In reality it is not. It is part of me. It is made up of my own cells and plugged into my blood supply. Its fast growth rate is one of the reasons I have lost weight and am so tired, my body feeding these traitorous cells like a demanding baby. Even so, I continue to think of it as something foreign; an alien body to be dealt with and removed.

The fact that the tumour was definitely malignant was conveyed to us the day after the operation. Fiona felt its impact much more keenly, partly because she understood more of the implications and partly because I was still woozy from morphine. I remember the two of us discussed it for some time before visiting time ended and she had to leave.

While I lay in bed with all the medical attention I needed, she returned home to explain the news to the children and sort out the practicalities of home life. Her incredible self-sufficiency is a constant amazement to me and I confess to being the undeserving beneficiary of her household management skills. But this particular night was a particularly low point for her, leaving me so weak in hospital and bearing the consequences of malignancy in her mind. She could not bring herself to circulate the news that evening and when she finally went to bed it was not to a restful sleep. Even so, she felt the support of friends and family in prayer and in practical ways, and something of God's peace.

I have concentrated a lot on my own suffering but it was shared by Fiona in a very real sense. There is something tangible in man and wife being 'one body' and just as my body was damaged, so was she. It was never only my problem. Throughout, Fiona was with me at consultations and knew more about what was going on than I did. In a sense she 'managed' my illness for me, alleviating the practicalities from my shoulders. She is a natural carer and I think finds greater comfort in the busyness of practical help than in too much time to contemplate. I owe her a debt in many ways, though it is one I doubt I can ever repay. Not that she expects me to, our debts being cancelled in advance when we promised 'in sickness and in health' all those years ago.

The strength of Fiona's ability to cope is, like many strengths, also a source of weakness. Many people have offered to help out but she copes so well it is often not necessary. We then worry that the rejection might offend and sometimes even catch ourselves trying to think of things for people to do to make them feel better, as if we are at fault for not being more in need. The overall effect is probably that we are less close to people than we might otherwise be. Acts of kindness done for friends draws people together and maybe we lose something in managing so well. Certainly Fiona feels this sometimes in terms of friendships. In fact, the one help that we did identify, quite late in the day as it happens, is simply that of being a friend to Fiona. Just spending time with her to chat and listen to how she felt was a great way of expressing practical friendship and I regret that we did not realise the value of it sooner. But we are grateful to those who gave it anyway, without being asked.

So, malignant it was, though with many questions still to be answered. Analysis of the bits of tumour removed would, we were told, take a couple of weeks. I think it would help patients greatly if someone were to put together a simple dictionary of medical jargon. The definition of 'a couple of weeks' would be something like, 'A general term meaning an unknown period, ranging from two weeks to infinity, often associated with periods of anxious waiting'. Perhaps this should be my next project.

FROM:	**FIONA MAGGS**
DATE:	**9 JULY 2005**
TO:	**OUR NETWORK OF FRIENDS AND FAMILY**
SUBJECT:	**SURPRISE!**

Just to let you know that Chris has come home today! It is a big surprise considering he was only moved off the HDU on Thursday afternoon.* He had his last drain and drip taken out on Friday morning and then was fully independent. Following an x-ray and blood tests the doctors decided he was well enough to come home today and Chris was very eager to come. He is obviously very weak and tired but now just needs to regain some strength ready for the next treatment.

I'm sure that lots of your prayers have been answered as it is quite amazing to think that 3 days ago he was attached to all sorts of machines and monitors.

Thank You

Fiona   ** Two days earlier.*

A GOOD NIGHT'S SLEEP

Sleep is a wonderful invention. I don't know why children take such little pleasure in it and always try to push their bedtimes later. It is not until you are well into adult life that you really start to appreciate it, and then find you can't get enough. Or, like me, illness disturbs the routine of regular slumber and leaves you pining for the long, deep sleep that used to leave you so refreshed.

Back home I had hoped that things would improve after the bustle of the hospital ward. It was certainly quieter but sleep remained difficult. I was, naturally, tired most of the time because of the effects of the operation and often took to dozing during the day. This was a habit that would be with me for many months, though I could never quite shake off the feeling that it was a bad one, associating it with laziness, self-indulgence and (thanks to my father) old age. I also worried that daytime sleep would make it harder to sleep at night, a bit like spoiling your dinner by eating between meals. None of these were particularly rational thoughts. The medical advice was to sleep as often as the need arose. Nevertheless, the concerns lingered.

When the need for sleep was strongest, I took to bed. Here I restricted myself to no more than two hours at a time for fear of wasting my life away; a pointless fear since my waking hours were largely spent in just passing the time idly anyway. At other times I attempted to sleep in an armchair or curled up on a sofa. Neither of these were entirely satisfactory in terms of comfort but that suited me in some ways, the discomfort acting as a natural periodic reminder that I was indulging in 'improper' behaviour and should rouse myself as soon as the heaviness behind the eyes had cleared.

Whatever the location, sleep seemed to come in short packages. The need to close my eyes was overwhelming at times and the initial pleasure of lying down and doing so gave me a warm comfort that ought naturally to have led to sleep. Sometimes it would and other times I would hang around awkwardly outside semi-consciousness, like an adolescent teenager waiting for a girl who wouldn't show.

Either way, time would abandon its clockwork reliability to skip at an irregular pace so that I had no idea how much had passed without looking at my watch. Sometimes it would have dragged, other times it would have raced. One moment of sleep could be a minute or twenty or sixty. They all felt the same, the only indication of how much time had passed being the amount of saliva dribbled onto the pillow.

At night I was often restless. Posture was vital to success. Before being ill I had become reliant on one particular sleeping position. This involved lying on my front, with only a thin pillow and one arm above my head; a sort of informal recovery position. The operation left me stranded on my back and, in hospital at least, propped up on several pillows. My chest was too sensitive to lie on initially and even later on I found I could not sleep on my front for months because my breathing would become so shallow that my body would wake me up to complain about the lack of oxygen. So new sleeping postures began to be adopted and particular positions became favourites. The trouble was that moving in my sleep, which the body does quite naturally, inevitably woke me up as some part of my bruised torso would sound the alarm.

This restlessness was not just physical. Mentally I found I often could not relax at night. For some time after coming out of hospital my head would be very active when I was trying to sleep, following weird ideas that would be equally compelling and frustrating. Often silly but intense storylines would run through the night, carrying on in periods of being half awake and somehow becoming more real as a result. Add to that a tendency for leg twitching and it was not surprising that Fiona took herself off elsewhere when it all got too disturbing for her.

A technique recommended by a friend for relaxing in hospital before going to sleep was to listen to a story on CD. I took this up both in hospital and at home, though not with great success. For a start the personal CD player I borrowed from my son was a little sensitive and caused a few frustrations when it jumped or refused to play. And then there was my choice of CDs. Our friend had offered us a number from her range. I turned down the Harry Potter option in favour of the more serious and 'worthy'. So I waded my way through Thomas Hardy's 'Tess of the D'Urbervilles' and 'Far from the Madding Crowd', plus Emily Bronte's 'Wuthering Heights' and finally 'Rebecca' by Daphne Du Maurier. It would be difficult to imagine a set of stories less likely to raise the spirits, with misery and tragedy the core themes in them all. I may have ended up more relaxed but I think I was more morose as well.

Night time can often feel a lonely place. It is dark and quiet, and even those close to you are no longer companions as they lie senseless in their own world of dreams. The songs recorded in the Bible in Psalms often refer to the night as a special time to meditate on God. All the activities of daily life have stopped and a sleepless night can be an opportunity to listen to God. I certainly did so on a few occasions, though probably far fewer than I ought.

About a week after coming out of hospital I found myself sitting on the side of the bed at 3 a.m. trying to decide what to do.

I knew lying down again would continue to disturb Fiona and would not bring me sleep but I did not want to get up either. So I found myself on my knees, praying. I did not pray for myself. I think God knew enough about my problems from the prayers of others and my own frequent cries for help. Instead I prayed for friends and family who were praying for me. It was good to think of them all, each with their own situations and issues and bring them all before God.

The immediate result, once I had finished, was a successful bowel movement (which I always see as a positive) and finding a comfortable position in which to sleep. But it led into a conversation with Fiona the following morning in which she said that fears over the future had been very much on her mind during the night.

Once the children had gone to school we sat down and spent some time talking, crying and praying together. It was one of those moments when emotions were let loose for a while before being filed away again in order to get on with the day-to-day challenges. God was central to such times. It was not just me against the world, or even Fiona and me. It was the three of us.

I did not pray at 3 a.m. every morning. Many nights passed with only selfish calls for relief. It was around this time that I got a letter from Tom Duncanson, a former minister of ours. His words were very helpful and full of compassion. He enclosed a card on which was written a prayer from the Northumbria Community. It captured my feelings perfectly and I prayed it many times in the following weeks as I turned off the light.

Calm me, O Lord, as you stilled the storm.
Still me, O Lord, keep me from harm.
Let all the tumult within me cease.
Enfold me, Lord, in your peace.

FROM:	FIONA MAGGS
DATE:	21 JULY 2005
TO:	OUR NETWORK OF FRIENDS AND FAMILY
SUBJECT:	WHAT'S NEXT?

It has been a couple of weeks since I emailed to let you know what was going on but I have been waiting to have something to tell you! Chris is slowly recovering from his operation although is finding it frustrating that it is very slow. His scar is healing very well but he is still coming out in bruising and still developing aches and pains which we hope are from the surgery.

We have been waiting for an appointment to come through to go back and see the surgeon to get the results of the tests they have done on the tissue they removed and to find out whether they are going to do chemotherapy or radiotherapy. This week there have been a number of phone calls and today we have eventually found out that due to the complicated nature of the tumour they have asked a professor at the Royal Marsden Hospital in London to look at it. This means more delay so we will not have an answer for probably another week.

We have to believe that all of this is in God's hands and although our human nature wants everything sorted quickly, God is still in control. Please continue to pray for peace and patience for us both. The children finish school tomorrow so we enter another different phase with the children being around all day. Remember them as they are missing out on their trip to America which they were very excited about.

I shall let you all know when we finally get our long awaited news.

Fiona

A FIRST TIME FOR EVERYTHING

I remember sitting in bed in hospital a few days after the operation, wanting to come home, thinking how much better I was feeling. By then, I had done the basics like walking and going to the toilet. I had even managed a tentative bath. I thought I was ready for the outside world but I had a lot to learn. Recovering from major surgery was to take a long time and my body was very fragile. As we drove away from the hospital I felt the seat belt pressing against my tender chest. Every movement of the car seemed to jolt my body and trigger my supersensitive pain receptors. It was a relief to get home and settle into a stationary comfy chair.

For several days I happily played the role of an invalid, sleeping, sitting and eating being my main occupations. The weather was hot and we entertained several visitors in the back garden. I sat in state with our guests feeling sorry for me while Fiona did all the work. I could have got used to it given more time.

One of my few regular responsibilities in the household is making sandwiches in the morning for the children to take to school for lunch. I had continued in my duty up to going into hospital and this was the first job I resumed as part of my recovery. Eight days after the operation I was downstairs early enough to perform the task. It was a small contribution to normal family life but it meant something to me.

Actually, when I think about it, the whole sandwich making thing is probably highly symbolic regardless of being ill. Fiona is in charge of all matters to do with running the house. She organises cleaning, washing, purchases, cooking, decorating, gardening and probably other things that I cannot even think of.

The rest of us generally get enlisted for specific tasks, commensurate with our abilities. I am sufficiently qualified to make sandwiches, the main requirement being that of getting up in the morning. Despite the fact that Fiona thinks about the necessary sandwich ingredients, goes out and buys them and provides the other lunch box contents, I still cling to the belief that my sandwich making role is pivotal to the provision of our children's mid-day nutrition and somehow fulfils my duty of care as a parent. So, to me, it was more than a few bits of sliced bread stuffed with wafer thin chicken that morning. My first round of sandwiches proved I was on my way back to being a fully functioning provider for the family.

That same day I achieved two other firsts. I shuffled all the way down the road to the doctor's surgery with Fiona, my first trip out of the house. Admittedly I needed a rest in the waiting room when we arrived but we spent some time chatting with the doctor and a lady from church who worked there. The objective of the journey was to pick up another sick note, signing me off work for several more weeks. In time the doctor simply wrote 'until further notice' to save us both the paperwork.

The other achievement was to wash up. I could not load or empty the dishwasher at this stage as it involved bending down but standing at the sink was within my grasp. Such normality was another step in the right direction and every one of these small tasks was a proud achievement.

The following day saw my first trip to the shops; a ride out to Matalan. I am not an enthusiastic shopper, especially for clothes. Loitering while Fiona explores the ladies' section of Marks & Spencer or Next or any number of other similar retail outlets is virtually unequalled in terms of mind-numbing tedium. I have occasionally tried to take an interest, noting the different styles and colours and thinking about what might suit but such efforts quickly wane.

It is like trying to listen with interest to the weather reports on the radio. However much I try, I cannot sustain my attention to the end of the forecast. I tell myself it is because there is simply too much weather-based information in quick succession and being unable to take it all in I simply give up. Perhaps it is the same with ladies' fashions; too much choice to cope with.

The men's areas in such shops are considerably smaller, perhaps catering to the lower capacity of the typical man for variety, but even here I find myself floundering. You would think that since I am looking for myself I would be more absorbed but often I still cannot muster sufficient interest. A wide range of shirts and t-shirts are dismissed with, "I'm okay for tops at the moment" and I move on, rather aimlessly, meandering more in the general direction of the exit than anywhere else. Except, of course, the exit from the men's area takes us back into the ladies' area again and it is a case of out of the frying pan into the fire.

So perhaps it is not surprising that my first trip to the shops is not a great success. After ten minutes looking at men's trousers I retreat to the car, exhausted, while Fiona continues with the full circuit and no doubt some trophies in the form of items to try out at home. Inevitably she will take most of them back because they are not quite right; a routine I would find overwhelmingly depressing since it takes you round in circles, though she never seems to tire of it.

My first trip to church was just short of two weeks after the operation. It was the first time I had been with a large group of people and talked so much. My voice was croaky and got weaker fairly quickly but it was great to be among so many friends and to feel their concern and care. Sunday mornings were times I would come to look forward to greatly over the following months, not just as a social outlet (which they certainly were) but also as part of getting back to a normal routine.

Church on Sunday has always been in my life and I consider it a precious gift to join with fellow Christians in a weekly time dedicated to worshipping and thinking about God.

Some people at church have told me they thought I was ever so brave to be there virtually every week throughout it all. It is kind of them to say so but my automatic instinct was to be with my church family and I think I took greater strength from them than they took from me.

FROM:	**FIONA MAGGS**
DATE:	**5 AUGUST 2005**
TO:	**OUR NETWORK OF FRIENDS AND FAMILY**
SUBJECT:	**UPDATE ON CHRIS**

Thought I had better bring you up to date on what is happening in the Maggs household. Actually in terms of progress with the tumour, there has been none. We are still waiting for the results to come back from the Royal Marsden. We were told that they would be a week and it is now over two weeks. We are frustrated. We do have an appointment to see the surgeon next Thursday (11th) but that is the follow up from the operation.

We have made two visits back to the hospital that were unscheduled. Chris's wound now has an infection and is leaking so we have been back twice for the doctors to look at it and take swabs. The district nurse is coming in and dressing the wound. He has had three lots of different antibiotics but after two weeks things have still not healed up. We are awaiting the nurse again today and will see what we are going to do next. In himself, Chris is a little better and able to concentrate more and do a little more. He still gets very tired and breathless so is spending a lot of time sitting with the occasional trip out but not very far. He did try to drive the car last week but discovered it used muscles and pulled all over his body, so he continues to be a passenger!

I hope that brings you up to date. We are spending a lot of time waiting. Please continue to pray, especially that we would get the results very soon and that the doctors would have a clear idea of treatment. I do promise that when we get our appointment, or if we get news next Thursday we will let you all know.

Fiona

THE WEEPING WOUNDED

For a couple of weeks after the operation I could feel myself getting physically stronger each day. However, I was still not having any treatment for the tumour, the remnant of which continued to grow inside me. The symptoms of coughing, breathlessness, hot sweats and losing weight were still there and soon outweighed any benefits of recovery from the operation itself. It was logical that this would happen but even so a sense of despair hit me when I realised that I was deteriorating again rather than improving. It was not helped by the disappointment of delays in test results and the prospect of treatment remaining some weeks away.

Then I noticed that the top of the scar running down my chest had become red and swollen. A trip to the doctor's left some uncertainty as to whether there was an infection or not but a course of antibiotics was prescribed as a precaution. Tablets seem to be the solution to nearly everything in medicine. I was taking tablets as a result of the operation to relieve the pain, to top up my iron and for constipation (caused by the painkillers and iron tablets). These had to be taken three or four times a day with food and now the antibiotics were twice a day on an empty stomach. Other even more complicated regimes would follow and I can understand how easily people get confused about it all and take the wrong ones at the wrong time. I wrote it all down, setting my watch alarm several times during the day for the next dose.

Some people may be more relaxed about such things but I was determined to get it absolutely right, reading and following the instructions to the letter. In fact, I got quite annoyed about one set of tablet instructions because I thought they were not precise enough. The instruction said they should be taken at least two hours after food or at least one hour before food. It was the word 'or' I objected to. Surely the intention was to ensure that the tablet hit an empty stomach and had an hour to do its work before any other food came along, so it should be 'and' not 'or'. Otherwise, you need only obey one of the alternatives. So, if you took a tablet immediately after a meal, on a full stomach, but did not eat anything else for at least an hour then you satisfied the second requirement. Or, you could take a tablet on an empty stomach, satisfying the first requirement, then eat straight away. I don't think either of these was intended and got quite wound up about it. I appreciate clarity and this wonton lack of it upset me.

For anyone equally enamoured with precision, can I recommend insurance documents as a good read. My favourite was a booklet circulated through our children's school offering recompense for any physical injuries suffered by pupils. The detailed description of what constituted the loss of a digit or limb was beautiful but my favourite touch was clarification that a claim for the £100,000 death benefit precluded consecutive claims for bodily injury. So, in the event of a freak accident during a technologies lesson, you could not, for example, claim the death benefit plus loss of an eye and a severed finger.

This passion for accuracy runs through many aspects of my life. For example, I become quite distraught when apostrophes get missed off or put where they should not be. The rules of grammar (or at least the ones I recognise and understand) are there to be followed.

It is the same with board games, the rules having to be followed to the letter. I will never be one of those doting grandparents who let their grandchildren win every game of snakes and ladders by bending the rules. They will quickly learn that a game with granddad is a lesson in life's harsh realities, and probably choose to play with their grandmother instead.

So the tablets were taken on time and in accordance with instructions as much as possible. Even so, they did not always work. I woke one night with a damp patch on my chest. At first I assumed it was another hot sweat (an effect of the tumour) but further investigation revealed that I was leaking a mixture of pus and blood from the swollen scar. Fiona patched me up temporarily but the leak continued to dribble over the next couple of days.

So we returned to the doctor's and they sent us back to the hospital ward. It was unpleasant to go back, though it is difficult to say why I disliked it so much. Perhaps it was because it reinforced that feeling of getting worse again, returning physically to the ward emphasising my slide back into poorer health.

In fact, the return visit turned out to be most helpful. The doctor who saw us checked the wound thoroughly, squeezed a lot of liquid out, took a swab to identify the infection and prescribed a stronger antibiotic (which had to be taken four times a day, one hour before meals, so my daily routine had to be rescheduled again). But the greatest benefit for us was in being able to ask some questions about my recovery from the operation.

When I had left the ward, just four days after surgery, I was given little idea what to expect. The surgeon had indicated it would take two or three weeks for me to recover, though he said my chest bone would not knit together for twelve weeks. Perhaps we should have asked what he meant by 'recover'. To a surgeon it may just have meant that I would be well enough to go back under the knife. My expectations were probably too high. They were certainly higher than my experience, so it was good to get a review of progress and a reality check on this occasion. The doctor explained that it would take two months for my breathing to return to normal because the pain in my chest area would be around for that long. He said that weight gain was also a few weeks away because at this stage the proteins were being washed away by my body as a reaction to the stress it had been put through.

Fiona and I both felt much better about things after this, simply because we now understood some of the processes going on inside me. It would have been helpful to have had more of an indication when I was first discharged; an explanation sheet setting out broad timescales for recovery and what to look out for in terms of danger signs. I never thought about it at the time, my eagerness to get out of hospital at least as keen as the hospital's eagerness to get my bed ready for the next patient. I do remember being surprised at the lack of physiotherapy advice. I had expected some exercises to perform to aid recovery, or at least some instructions on what to avoid. But no, there was nothing; not even a follow up appointment for over a month.

For me, although this lack of aftercare was frustrating, it was not a great problem. I was well catered for in that Fiona is an occupational therapist and I could not have been in better hands. There must, though, be many people far less fortunate who get into difficulties if this lack of basic follow-through care is systematic. The long-term medical benefits of providing information surely outweigh the immediate costs of producing it. But perhaps the NHS, like most institutions, is no longer set up to make such judgements. Everything these days is focussed on departmental budgets and a cost in one area to relieve a burden elsewhere has little chance of being approved. The common good of the organisation has been sacrificed to the principle of 'each to his own'; market forces replacing common sense and the plot being lost somewhere along the way. In this case, the plot involves very sick people and it is lives that are potentially being lost.

The stronger antibiotics failed to clear up the wound infection and a week later I was told to report back to the hospital ward, this time with the possibility of being readmitted. My heart sank at the prospect and I had another of those emotional crises, leaking behind the eyes as well as from the wound. There were now two visible holes at the top of my scar where stitches had pulled apart and their concern was that the infection was quite deep. An X-ray proved this not to be the case though, and I returned home with another longer course of antibiotics.

In all it took five courses of antibiotics and several weeks to clear the infection. It was never a serious medical problem but emotionally it was draining at a time when we were anxiously waiting for news on the tumour. It drove us to prayer! I confess I am not a good prayer and we have never had regular family times of domestic intercession. But Fiona and I found great comfort in praying together at the end of each day during this particular stage. It is a routine we have failed to maintain and I cannot adequately explain why. Perhaps it is because praying together requires a certain intimacy that is not always there at the end of the day's activities. It is one of those things I would recommend but rarely live up to myself.

While on the area of prayer, it is worth recounting an incident that took place one night at this time. We had turned off the light around 11 p.m. but about midnight Fiona and I were both still awake. I was restless and my coughing would not settle down. In fact, it was getting worse and we were both concerned. Perhaps the night emphasises such feelings but I began to despair at the further journeying we yet had to do and the length of time it was all taking.

During a respite in the coughing we prayed together and, as the praying was ending, it occurred to me to try the cough medicine that had been so effective months ago before the operation. It did the trick. Many would put this down to coincidence but it is just one of many small examples where we felt that God intervened.

But the episode also made me realise just how strong the frustration over my deteriorating health was. I made light of it most of the time, even convincing myself that I was not worried, but it lurked beneath the surface. For Fiona and I, bringing those honest feelings before God in prayer was a great relief and soothed my troubled mind as much as the cough medicine soothed my throat.

FROM: **FIONA MAGGS**
DATE: **11 AUGUST 2005**
TO: **OUR NETWORK OF FRIENDS AND FAMILY**
SUBJECT: **PROGRESS!**

Today we have had our follow up appointment at Heartlands Hospital. We saw a very helpful and informative doctor who went to a lot of trouble finding out information and making a lot of telephone calls.

The wound continues to leak and although none of the swabs have grown anything he is sure there is some infection still there and so another longer course of antibiotics has been prescribed. The results are still not back from the Royal Marsden due to the fact that they are also having trouble identifying the tumour and have done a number of tests but not yet the one that gives the necessary answer. They hope that the test they are doing at the moment will give a definite answer by the middle of next week. Chris has therefore been referred to an Oncologist and this afternoon we had a phone call from the doctor we saw this morning giving us all the details of what is going to happen next. We are to have an appointment next week (waiting for that in the post or by phone) to discuss the diagnosis (which hopefully will be confirmed by then) and the treatment which looks like it will be chemotherapy. At last some progress.

That is all we know so far. Looks like we may start to have a few more appointments within the next few weeks and so please do continue to pray for us as we face our next challenge. Chris is starting to feel a little stronger but is still breathless and gets tired very quickly. Pray that his recovery from the surgery would continue and that the chemotherapy would be successful.

Fiona

PASSING THE TIME

There are certain times and events that stand out over the weeks and months of my illness but in between these key moments lie large stretches of non-eventful days.

I am always amazed by the scale of outer space. The distances between planets are incredible. We rarely get a sense of them because pictorial representations of our solar system bunch up the planets in order to get them on the same page. If they were drawn to scale on a single page, with the correct distances between them, the planets would be so small we would hardly see them. Distances between stars are on a different scale again, each with vast quantities of empty space between them. Human travel between the heavenly bodies is impractical not so much because of the technology but because of the timescale. My medical progress sometimes felt like that, with time stretching out endlessly before the next appointment.

The gaps in between had to be filled though. I was obviously restricted in what I could achieve physically and, for much of the time, mentally too. There was a fuzziness in my head that discouraged concentration and left me lacking in creativity, or even the will to be creative. I have always enjoyed writing but now this seemed too demanding a task. I turned to more passive occupations.

Films were a great way to pass a couple of hours. I get totally absorbed in a film, putting life on hold for the duration to take in the story. The cinema experience is best of course, your eyes and ears fully focussed on the film, the only distraction being other viewers chomping their way through popcorn, packets of crisps and other confectionery. Personally, I would ban all food and drink in the cinema but perhaps I'm a bit of a purist. I'd also refuse re-entry to anyone who goes to the toilet. A little bit of planning in the bladder department is all it takes!

Not being up to cinema trips, videos and DVDs were my usual source of entertainment, though viewing was rarely uninterrupted. Fiona dislikes films generally, not least because of their length. Her preferred viewing time is half an hour. As far as she's concerned anything longer smacks of indulgence and can rarely be justified. So much of the film watching took place when she was out, making it seem somewhat furtive.

My favourite films generally involve action, dry humour and often a little weirdness. Anything with Clint Eastwood in generally satisfies the first two but heroes with super powers tend to feature high on my list as well. I tried the Godfather trilogy but found it too drawn out and depressing. The Matrix trilogy is more my sort of thing. If you are going to suspend belief to enter into the world of a film why use the same old world we live in? Variations on reality seem to me far more interesting and engaging than the ups and downs of relationship drama. And any film that leaves you wanting to watch it again to understand what it was all about seems to me to have done a great job. So I would happily escape into fictional worlds for the duration of the adventure, unless interrupted by telephone calls or window cleaners or Fiona's unexpected return.

There were many far less interesting activities. We tend to keep things 'just in case'. This includes baby equipment stored in the loft, old furniture transferred to the garage, textbooks long since redundant, ornaments and pictures out of favour, etc. We are never precise about what the 'just in case' might be and, of course, it never actually occurs. Or if it does, we miss it because we have forgotten the relevant item is there. Then, at some later date, we rediscover it and think, "That would have been useful when...". The sensible thing to do at that point would be to throw it away but, no, we do the opposite and value it even more because it has proved that it would have been useful. So we keep it.

The same process applies to paper items such as receipts, wage slips, instruction manuals and so on. Thankfully, their minimal occupation of space means they are easier to store but the counter balance is that we rarely feel the need to review what is there. It was Fiona's idea that I should occupy myself sorting through the receipts folder. It is one of those accordion style folders, spilt into sections and expandable to alarming dimensions. Over the years it had grown sufficiently to fill the whole of a filing cabinet draw.

To be honest, it was a job I did not mind at all. Paperwork is what I do best and sorting through these remnants of our family history was not too taxing at all. In fact, I got enthusiastic enough to start a catalogue on the computer of our household possessions. Insurance companies always suggest it's a good idea but I doubt many people ever get around to it. After all, it would only ever be of any use if the house burnt down and everything got destroyed, in which case the computer would probably be gone too. And anyway, you never think it's going to happen to you. I suppose it's a bit like not getting around to making a will (which was something else we thought I really ought to do).

Inevitably we had receipts for items we no longer owned, or at least could no longer remember owning, though they are probably stored away in the loft or the garage. There were problems with receipts that did not specify the item. What did we purchase for £12.99 from Argos in 1986? I told myself I had to be ruthless and throw that one away. I even, reluctantly, disposed of my work expenses slips if they were over ten years old. I have never needed to refer back to any of them – but you never know.

For sentimental reasons I kept some things; my first week's wage slip for example, paid in cash. I knew I really ought to throw away the gas and electric bills since some of them related to our previous house and a few to the house before that, which we left in 1989. Even so, I could not resist recording the meter readings on a spreadsheet and working out how our consumption had changed over the years. Throwing away such data forever would have been scandalous.

Then there were the credit card statements going back twenty years. When we first got married and set up home in 1983 we used to budget meticulously. There were set monthly amounts allocated for food, clothes, utilities, household goods, a holiday fund and so on. This was purely practical in that we had no savings and needed to live within our means. We can afford to be less precise now but part of me still hankers for the financial detail of those times. To be able to say to the penny how much we had spent on leisure items in a year has a lingering appeal and it was this latent desire that held me back from destroying the evidence.

Wouldn't it be good, I thought, to go through all those credit card statements and the cheque book stubs (yes, we had kept those too) and itemise expenditure? It would be a massive job and I could not really think of a good reason why it was worth doing but at the same time neither could I bring myself to throw everything away. In the end I compromised by creating another spreadsheet recording total annual expenditure on each credit card before shredding the documents. I doubt it will ever be of any use but over the years I will come across it every now and then and smile.

I have another vice to admit to, though I am somewhat reluctant. Nevertheless, I did say I wanted this account to be honest and for that reason I must confess. I know it is not manly, and I would never do it in public, but a good deal of time was spent with needle and thread doing cross-stitch. In my defence, it is a hobby I started for marital reasons. Fiona has always been good at crafts and would often cross-stitch or knit in an evening when we were first married. I preferred to read a book but discovered that the two occupations did not match. Fiona would talk while working and I could not read and listen at the same time, despite my best attempts. So I took up cross-stitch in order to keep the peace.

Of course, I don't do the flowery stuff. My first project during my illness was a steam train. I think there was a whole series of trains if I'd had the inclination but to be honest machinery in cross-stitch does nothing for me and I left it after one. Next was a butterfly with, I admit, some lavender, but this was for my mother's 70th birthday and I think that is adequate excuse. After that I wanted a bigger challenge. I accompanied Fiona to various craft outlets in pursuit of a suitable theme but the choice was limited. Most were decidedly 'girlie' and the remainder consisted of tigers or sad looking dogs. In the end we settled on a Tuscan scene.

It is interesting to note people's reactions to this pastime. The ladies usually say something along the lines of "Oh, you are clever". I doubt they would say the same to a woman. Cross-stitch is not particularly clever or creative, you just follow a pattern. It is the combination of being a man and achieving this basic level of domestic competence that they are complimenting. Men, rarely say anything. They just avert their eyes and shake their heads pityingly.

FROM:	**FIONA MAGGS**
DATE:	**18 AUGUST 2005**
TO:	**OUR NETWORK OF FRIENDS AND FAMILY**
SUBJECT:	**WE HAVE A DIAGNOSIS!!**

We have had another appointment today, this time with an Oncologist at the Walsgrave Hospital in Coventry. At last we have been given a diagnosis. Apparently the samples have been to two hospitals in London who have both done tests and come up with the same result. Chris has Hodgkin's (Follicular) Lymphoma. It just seems that the tumour had other tissues in it and was in a difficult place which made the diagnosis problematic. Anyway he is to start chemotherapy hopefully next week after having a bone marrow biopsy. This is booked for Tuesday morning and they hope that the chemo will start by the end of the week. He will have chemo every two weeks for six months and then will need radiotherapy as well. The chemo has the usual side effects of hair loss and sickness/nausea + other rarer things. He will need to be careful of infections as his immunity will be reduced. So if you have chicken pox or you have seen anyone with it we won't want to see you!

Chris will also have a body scan hopefully next week or the week after to check whether the lymphoma is affecting anywhere else or if it is just confined to his chest area. He is going to need lots of blood tests and regular scans. The therapy will be given at Walsgrave but they hope that they will be able to arrange for some things to happen at the Alexandra Hospital in Redditch which is much closer to us (probably the blood tests).

The oncology unit is very nice with a lovely waiting area and a calm atmosphere. They are moving to a new hospital in two weeks time so we may only have one treatment in the old unit and then we will see their new unit which I would assume will be even nicer.

Chris and I are feeling OK at the moment. I think that we have waited so long for the diagnosis that it was just a relief to get it. I sort of felt like we should be upset but it is just great to feel that the waiting is over. Chris is of course concerned about the treatment (although the children are already teasing him about losing his hair. Tim has offered to lend him his beanie hat) and all that that entails. For someone who does not like hospitals he is certainly getting plenty of experience.

Looks like our prayer request will be ongoing for some time as we have at least another 8 months to go yet. Thank you for all your support and prayers so far. Please remember us next week as we start treatment and enter another phase of this time of our life. Pray for the children that they would continue to cope with our different life style. Pray for Chris as he is still getting over the operation and has a long way to go. Pray for me as I juggle it all!

Thanks a lot
Fiona

JOIN THE CLUB

So now, at last, it had a name – a Hodgkin's Lymphoma. It turned out the chest specialist who saw me back in May was right in his first assessment, though it took months to get an accurate diagnosis. It was not as rare as they had thought, which I found disappointing. With all the attention I was getting I felt a responsibility to have something seriously unusual. Alas, this was not the case. The diagnosis had been complicated because the tumour was mixed together with my thalamus gland. Apparently it is a gland operational in childhood and no longer of any use but it hangs around in the chest and in my case caused some confusion. It got in with the wrong crowd, as my mother would say.

A lymphoma is, as the name suggests, a cancer of the lymphatic system, which they explained was a bit like the blood system in that it has a network throughout the body. It transports tissue fluids (lymph), including certain white blood cells, back from around the body and eventually returns them to the blood stream. (I had no idea there was another system like the blood system and find myself wondering indignantly what other systems my body might be operating without my knowledge.)

There was obviously concern that cancerous cells may have travelled from the tumour through the lymphatic system. Hence the bone marrow biopsy and body scan. If the cancer had spread in this way to secondary sites the prognosis was not good and I suppose I should have been worried. I don't recall that I was though. It would be nice to put this down to a super-spiritual sense of peace from God but it would only be half the story and I cannot even take any credit for that. Looking back I recognise that the prayers of friends and family carried us through that time and gave us a supernatural peace but I confess as well to some degree of ignorance of the dangers.

Giving it a medical name did nothing to improve my mental perception of the enemy within. However, a couple of days after the diagnosis I got a much more palpable opportunity. A swelling appeared on my chest and proceeded to grow steadily. The tumour was pushing out between my ribs and I could touch it, hard under my skin. It was visible confirmation of something that had been hidden inside me for months. Being able to feel it was oddly comforting and disturbing at the same time. I found my hand frequently returning to the spot, to check on progress.

Once chemotherapy started, steroids were given to help reduce the tumour quickly. I woke one night to find the hardness had softened noticeably. I lay in bed pressing the spongy lump and listening to its squelching response. It was a very early physical sign of the treatment being successful and the swelling disappeared over a few days, as quickly as it had come. It was my only real tactile encounter with the cancer and lasted no more than three or four weeks but it marked the peak of the tumour's growth and the beginning of its decline and I am glad to have been able to make its acquaintance for that short time.

There is a surprising amount of literature available in relation to cancers. Each cancer type has its own leaflet and information sheet and there are many supplementary support groups. I picked up a leaflet on the Lymphoma Association, offering ongoing support to fellow sufferers and relatives. It made me smile to think that I was eligible to join a 'club' because of my cancer.

Joining clubs has always seemed to suggest a certain desire for status in my mind and the image of me proudly displaying my Lymphoma Association badge was not one I relished. On top of that, communal sharing in suffering is not for me. The thought of meeting up with fellow lymphomites (my own word) to run through symptoms and side effects did not appeal. I appreciate that there are those who greatly value such support and I applaud the work of those who provide it but I had no wish to dwell on my condition. I noticed that membership was for life – a somewhat reduced benefit for cancer sufferers.

There were also leaflets giving personal accounts of experiencing cancer. These I found most interesting. Personal stories say a lot more to me than medical information summaries. They revealed real people coping with real problems, not dissimilar to my own. And as a writer myself, I was intrigued by how much they chose to reveal. Some concentrated on treatment, others on feelings. All seemed to be upbeat and positive, encouraging the reader that the tough treatments for cancer are all worth it in the end. Writing my own account I feel pressure to do the same. I have no wish to dishearten anyone facing the harsh realities of cancer or other sufferings but at the same time I do not want to be falsely optimistic. Many cancer victims survive but many do not. The people who write the booklets are usually the former.

As I write now, a few months after treatment is finished, the signs are good but I am well aware that the tumour could return. My story is not one of miraculous healing. It is not even one of pulling through against the odds. We were told there was an 85% success rate for treating my type of cancer if it had not spread. That sounded pretty good to me, though as a statistician I know it is no guarantee. If I was in a room with twenty people with this type of lymphoma then probably three of us would die. Perhaps that's another reason why I'd rather not join a group consisting of fellow sufferers.

Hope is a good thing but I do not want to give false hope. I'd much rather give real hope, hope based on something fully reliable, hope based on something bigger than life and death itself. As a Christian I do have such a hope. I want my experience to point not to me but to God, who holds all things in his hands. I am happy to have my future in his care, whether I live or die. It is a safe pair of hands and his is a club worth joining.

FROM: **FIONA MAGGS**
DATE: **21 AUGUST 2005**
TO: **OUR NETWORK OF FRIENDS AND FAMILY**
SUBJECT: **UPDATE ON CHRIS**

Just to let you all know that Chris is going to start his chemotherapy treatment on Wednesday morning (9.30am appointment) at the Walsgrave Hospital.

Fiona

LIFE GOES ON

Surprisingly, the activities of family life do not all get put on hold when problems like illness strike. Although I was spending all my time wrapped up in treatment and convalescing, others in the family were busy in other more normal ways.

Our eldest son, Timothy, had been working hard on his AS levels. Or perhaps it would be more accurate to say he should have been working hard on his AS levels. He took the year-end exams in May and June and the results came out on 18 August. I will not record the grades achieved. Suffice to say his parents were disappointed and viewed the results as evidence that he should have listened when they told him he needed to revise. Tim, on the other hand, quickly readjusted his personal expectations and declared that he had done as well as he thought he would.

It would be some consolation to think that my illness had affected him in some way. Unfortunately, this was not true. Tim has always been as laid back about my condition as he is about everything else, to the point of being horizontal. We did hear of a scheme to adjust marks for exams upwards if the candidate had been suffering undue stress due to family illness or a dog dying or some other personal trauma. I don't know how such things can be measured given the different reactions of children to events. A stress monitor on Tim would be unlikely to register a pulse!

When confronted with better results achieved by others, Tim simply said, "But I bet they didn't have as much fun". If only schools had the forethought to award grades for the amount of fun achieved, Tim would have done so much better.

Luke remained similarly unruffled by events, although in his case this meant continued good work at school. My health was not a subject he discussed with anyone much. Every now and then on the way to school he would run into a chap down our road from the local tennis club. As Luke and I are both members our neighbour usually asked how I was doing, to which Luke would give a brief response. There would then be an awkward pause, following which he would tell Luke about his son, who had cancer some years ago and is fine now. Another awkward pause, then he would tell Luke to keep his chin up and they would part company. Somehow I managed to be a source of embarrassment to my son even through my illness.

Out of the three, Hannah was most disturbed by my illness. The older boys both went on action holiday weeks over the summer but Hannah's only planned holiday was our family trip to America, now cancelled. A good friend kindly offered to take her away for a week, staying with her parents down south. It did not work out well. Hannah was homesick and didn't like their food. She was returned half way through the week only to complain that it was boring back home.

At nine years old it is hard to control your worries, especially if you have a vivid imagination. Stories for girls of that age often feature orphans as the heroine and I suspect the unknown future played on her mind a lot, though she talked about it little.

Domestic duties still needed to be done. Luke took over the mowing of the lawn, on a cash in hand basis, but the garden got little attention otherwise. Friends helped with hedge trimming and the like to keep things from becoming overgrown but the flowerbeds were largely neglected.

Having said that, we probably spent more time just sitting in the garden and enjoying it during that summer than any other. We have a fairly large garden so much of our outdoor time is usually occupied with maintenance, the sitting and enjoying being restricted to occasional breaks for a cup of tea. This year we sat a lot, entertaining visitors outdoors and watching the plants (and weeds) grow. Nature seemed indifferent to our plight.

In fact, with 'Survival of the fittest' as its motto, nature probably looked on with scorn at our attempts to stop the natural course of events, both in the garden and in me. Life goes on but, for now, disease, death and decay are all part and parcel of its cruel cycle. God has promised a time when things will be different; when tears will be wiped away and there will be no suffering, no death. Nature itself will run by different rules. I look forward to sitting in the warmth of that day and not having to even think about the weeds.

FROM:	FIONA MAGGS
DATE:	24 AUGUST 2005
TO:	OUR NETWORK OF FRIENDS AND FAMILY
SUBJECT:	CHEMOTHERAPY

Well, Wednesday is nearly over and we have got through our two days of hospital treatment. The bone marrow biopsy went well yesterday without any problems. They sedated Chris and the pain was therefore bearable! It got a bit sore later in the day when the local anaesthetic wore off and is still a little tender.

Today we went for chemotherapy and it was a long day as this was the first time. We were there about 8 hours! The staff are really lovely and we were given lots of information and assurance and met our specialist Lymphoma nurse. Chris had to have other things as well as the chemo drugs but coped with it all. Unfortunately the tumour is now growing quite quickly and protruding from his chest. He is also on steroids to try and reduce some of the inflammation in the tumour. His haemoglobin is also so low that he has to go back in on Friday for a blood transfusion. That will again take all day. (Had to just stop the email writing as the sickness has just started!!!)

Please keep praying for Chris. His immune system is going to be knocked out and so he will be at risk of any infections. Pray for protection. He is anaemic and now definitely sick! All this makes him very weak and tired. We are both looking forward to a time when he has some energy and feels well.

It's time for me to go to bed now as I am also tired.
Fiona

P.S. His diagnosis is not follicular Hodgkin's lymphoma. It is nodular sclerosing Hodgkin's Lymphoma (with a thymic cyst). For those of you that way inclined you will have realised that the follicular type is a non-Hodgkin's lymphoma. The rest of you do not care!

It's in the blood

Chemotherapy is one of those things that most of us have heard of but, unless we have seen it in action, we have only vague ideas of what is involved. Blood transfusions are in a similar category. My expectation was largely based on a horror movie I saw a long time ago. The main character was a vampire who put himself into suspended animation when he needed to lie low. This involved lying in a red satin-lined coffin with tubes connected into his blood stream in both arms. A vivid yellow liquid started down one of the tubes and entered his body. Then the camera scanned across to the other side where we saw crimson-red blood oozing out to be stored in a large glass container. He was alone in a dark vault, accompanied only by eerie music.

The real thing turned out to be quite similar, except there was no coffin, no eerie music and no large glass containers filling up with blood. There was a tube going into one arm but nothing came out of the other. Both chemotherapy and blood transfusions are one-way transactions, the body having to use its own systems to dispose of the excess in the normal way. The drugs either come as bags of liquid, hung up on machines and drip fed into your blood stream over several hours, or in a syringe which is slowly injected into the tubing by a nurse.

My chemotherapy session started with a bag of saline solution. Then the four chemotherapy drugs were administered. Three were injected in and the fourth hung up on the machine. Most were translucent but one was bright red. Watching its steady progress through the tubes and into my body was the closest I got to my horror film image. This was the most powerful of the cocktail and knowing the damage it was designed to do added to the moment.

There are a wide range of chemotherapy drugs and which ones you get depends on your precise type of cancer. I had four because each one was designed to kill my reproducing cancer cells at different points in their cycle. Inevitably they do damage beyond the cancer and this causes the side effects.

The whole chemotherapy process took about three hours. There was no pain, other than getting the needle in to start with. Sometimes it went in straight away but other times there were problems. After the nurse had had two or three stabs at it they would ask someone else to have a go and if they could not do it the doctor was called in. The doctors were no better at it. In fact, they were often worse as they had less experience. But they had nobody to pass the buck to and so persevered until the job was done.

Of course, unlike my vampire role model I was not alone. The suite I attended was a large room with about ten high-backed cushioned chairs and one bed, spaced out along two long sidewalls. Everyone had come in for the day so we were all dressed in normal clothing and most had visitors sitting with them as well. It was a cosy community, all sharing the same unpleasant experience for the same dreadful reason but never really talking about it. We would pass the time of day, exchange weary sympathetic smiles and watch the bustling nurses go about their routines. Fiona got into a few conversations but I rarely did, preferring to close my eyes and rest, or absorb myself in the less taxing mental exercises offered by 'The Puzzler'.

The blood transfusion was a very long day. It took eight hours for the necessary units of blood to drip into me. At least I could feel I had paid my way on that one. I have been a blood donor for about twenty years, so hopefully I had banked at least as much as I was withdrawing. I will be making no more deposits now though. As a cancer sufferer I joined the long list of people whose blood is not up to scratch.

I will miss the experience. It is unique in being a gathering of people of all ages and types, voluntarily giving their own life-blood for the common good. There is something very British in the way we do it; sharing a common bond without ever acknowledging the person sitting or lying next to you.

Perhaps I could still attend and then tick the box that excludes me. "I'm sorry, sir, you cannot give blood. But you are welcome to have a cup of tea and a biscuit before you leave." It would allow me to watch the wonderful range of characters at least. But, no. I would worry that people thought I'd ticked one of the other boxes indicating less savoury behaviour. Perhaps the rejection would mark me out in the crowd as an outsider. No, I could not face the stigma. I will have to stay away and wear my blood donor tiepin to let everyone know I really am a good person inside. If I need more blood in the future, I just hope they operate an overdraft facility.

FROM:	FIONA MAGGS
DATE:	16 SEPTEMBER 2005
TO:	OUR NETWORK OF FRIENDS AND FAMILY
SUBJECT:	UPDATE ON CHRIS

Thought I would update you on what has happened in the Maggs household over the last few days. Chris has been back in hospital but has come out this evening. He is suffering from a side effect of the chemo. One of the drugs has affected the nerves in his intestines/bowels so everything has stopped! This has resulted in pain and vomiting and he has been feeling really dreadful this week. He is home and still feeling dreadful and being pumped with loads more drugs to counteract the other drugs he is being pumped with.

We do have some good news. The bone marrow biopsy showed that the lymphoma has not spread there and also the body scan seems to show that the lymphoma is just confined to his chest and has not spread to any other parts of his body. We see the doctor on Wednesday and will have the final details but she has also confirmed that Chris will have 6 cycles of treatment i.e. chemo for 6 months (we have done 1, so there are only 5 left!). We don't know yet about the radiotherapy.

Thanks for all your messages and prayers.
Fiona

HAIR TODAY, GONE TOMORROW

One thing everybody knows about chemotherapy is that you lose your hair. Actually, it is not 100% certain but the great majority do, so at least this was something I could be prepared for. We were told the hair loss would start about three weeks after the first treatment so we began a phased reduction in hair length to make the transition more gradual. The day after my first chemotherapy treatment we employed our newly purchased shaver kit to reduce the length.

I used to have long hair in my youth. Well, it was the seventies! As I got older it reduced in both length and density. I painfully remember my mother attacking my hair with the 'K-Tel Hair Thinner', a small plastic device with razor blades that seemed to operate by tugging hairs out by the roots. I am sure it could equally have been employed in a torture chamber. There were no such problems as I got older, my hair naturally thinning itself and a significant bald patch evolving. Now the chemotherapy was going to accelerate the process. I was offered a wig on the NHS, specifically made to replicate my own hairstyle. It would have been a terribly sad wig if I had taken up the offer.

The other preparation we made was the purchase of a head covering. These days, of course, a shaved head on a man is not unusual. In the past it would have immediately identified you as a thug or a cancer victim. Now it is fashionable and I would not have felt out of place in a crowd. Nevertheless, a head covering had practical uses. I was supposed to keep my head out of the sun and during the winter it would keep me warm.

The choice was limited. Headwear, to my mind at least, has a way of defining you. A flat cap made me a Yorkshire man, a deerstalker Sherlock Holmes, in a wide brimmed hat I was Australian. I admire those who can wear unusual headwear and keep their individuality but it does not work for me. I adopted the fairly universal baseball cap, wearing it the right way around for fear of being taken for an uncouth youth.

The prospect of hair loss was an easy laugh and there was a lot of joking with friends and family. It hid a painful insecurity that I hardly dared admit to myself. But sometimes, when the joking went too far I found it hurt. For example, when Hannah said she wouldn't want a bald dad picking her up from school my angry retort surprised both of us!

Hair has a lot to do with self-image and losing it meant losing something of who I thought I was. It is a relatively easy thing to deal with given time but my superficial lack of concern belied much deeper feelings. A good friend offered to stand alongside me by having his hair all shaved off. It was a well-intentioned thought but I felt it would only draw attention to my loss and asked him not to do it.

Around three weeks into the treatment I noticed more hairs appearing on the floor of the shower than normal. Then one night, after washing my hair in the bath and draining the water away, there they were – hundreds of hairs marooned at the bottom of the tub. It was nothing less than I should have expected but still it shocked me. Soon after that the hairs started appearing in large quantities on my pillow. I would wake to find it covered and had to spend time every day cleaning it off with sticky tape. I was starting to look decidedly patchy where my head rubbed at night. Fiona shaved me down to a 'number two'.

I never lost all my hair entirely. It quickly dwindled to nearly nothing though. Even shaved, the remnant looked odd, so people could not help but glance at it. They tried to do it subtly while in conversation but eyes are easily followed. It changes your appearance such a lot that it comes as a shock to anyone you have not seen for a while. When I popped into my workplace to say hello to a few people I was very conscious of my hair, or lack of it. It was the physical sign of my illness. It identified me as a victim and prompted many a sad, sympathetic, "Aaah". It remains the prominent badge of cancer sufferers worldwide, although ironically it is a symptom of the treatment rather than the disease.

There were other, less obvious, side effects. My weight dropped further when chemotherapy started. I was more than two and a half stone below normal and looked gaunt, bones showing through everywhere. Fiona took to calling me 'Stickman' as a term of endearment. I had been warned about trouble with soft tissues, which are more easily affected by the chemotherapy drugs. I started using a children's 'first toothbrush' so that I did not do damage to my gums. My taste buds changed. Sometimes it felt like my tongue was covered with a layer of something, like lime scale in a kettle, stopping me from tasting anything. The hospital recommended a saltwater mouthwash after each meal to reduce infection but it was so unpleasant I preferred to take the risk.

Sickness was not a regular problem, though there were certainly times when it was prominent. Tiredness was a constant companion, especially during the days following each treatment. Sleeplessness at night also featured strongly. Apparently I was grumpier as well, according to reliable sources in the family. Whether this was down to chemotherapy or stress or just age I could not say.

One other strange change took place around this time that I cannot adequately account for. I took an interest in cricket. In my normal state of mind, any game that can end in a draw after five days because they ran out of time needs a serious review. And yet here I was captivated by England's desperate attempts to win the Ashes. It is an aberration that thankfully lasted only a few weeks but it goes to show what damage those drugs can do to a man.

The immune system is severely disrupted by chemotherapy as well. Blood was taken a couple of days before each treatment and if any of the various levels tested was outside of the boundaries then treatment was postponed. It only happened once to me. My neutrophils (a type of white blood cell) were too low for my third visit and to counteract this I was given some injections. They had to be administered once a day for several days in each chemotherapy cycle. This was a new challenge for me but not for our family. Fiona has been an insulin-dependent diabetic for over twenty years and the number of injections she has given herself runs into thousands. So I could hardly make a fuss about a few for me.

The plan was that she would do the injections. After all, she was the expert. But when it came to it, it turned out that doing injections for yourself and doing them for someone else are quite different things. I guess a lot of nurses who inject other people would struggle with injecting themselves and Fiona found the same the other way around. So in the end I did it myself, simply following what I'd seen her do many times.

It is something I took a little pride in. Virtually all of my treatment was done by other people while I was the passive patient. People talk about cancer sufferers as being brave but I never felt I justified the accolade given that I did little to help or hinder the process. At least doing my own injections allowed me to feel I was participating, though whether it merits 'brave' I am still not convinced. I'd like to think I could get away with 'plucky cancer victim' though.

FROM:	FIONA MAGGS
DATE:	7 OCTOBER 2005
TO:	OUR NETWORK OF FRIENDS AND FAMILY
SUBJECT:	NEWS ON CHRIS

Just wanted to let you know that Chris is back in hospital again. He is suffering severe side effects of the chemo and is unable to keep anything down. He went into the Walsgrave on Thursday and they will be keeping him until at least Monday when they will be x-raying him again to see if his insides are behaving any better. Won't go into too much detail of what he is going through but I had to sit between him and the man in the next bed who were both throwing up! What a pleasant experience! Waited until I got out to the car to eat my sandwich.

Chris has his next chemo on Wednesday so he needs to get better for then. He managed to do his own injections before he went into hospital so we hope that his blood count will be OK. It may be that they have to alter his doses of chemo to try and avoid the problems he is having.

The rest of us are doing alright. I am very glad to have Chris' car to travel up and down to Coventry every day. His satellite navigation came in very useful when there was an accident on the M6 and after sitting for an hour I came off again and had to negotiate my way in the dark through the back of Coventry. That journey took me 2 hours rather than the usual 45 minutes.

Well it is way past my bed time and I definitely need it at the moment.

Thank you once again for all your concerns and prayers.

Fiona

JUST A GUT FEELING

I promised I would return to the subject of my bowels and I am as good as my word. The severe side effects tactfully skirted around in Fiona's email were pains and vomiting caused by a total paralysis of the bowel. It is a reaction to one of my chemotherapy drugs, typically seen in older people apparently. (Fiona says I have old man's bowels but I just think they are "special".)

The first time it happened they just upped the various laxatives but this second return to hospital was more serious. The bowel was swollen and could burst if not dealt with. They decided to keep me in until they saw some positive results. I did not have to stay in, of course. I had the option of discharging myself (no pun intended) but, as the doctor casually pointed out, a perforation of the bowel would probably kill me so they thought it best I stay under observation. It would have been churlish to disagree.

Medical science has progressed massively in many different areas but when it comes to bowel blockages the technique is probably about as ancient as you can get. Large doses of laxative are funnelled in at one end and copious amounts of water at the other.

My first enema was administered by a very efficient nurse. Having covered the bed with an incontinence sheet, "Just in case", she got me to adopt the position (lying on one side) and bare my rear end. "Try to relax," she said, as she attempted to ram a tube up my bottom. I failed to do so.

Once the plumbing was in place, a significant quantity of warm water was poured into my lower bowel. It was difficult to judge the precise amount from where I was experiencing it. The tube was removed and my anal muscles were called upon to retain the liquid. I was then instructed to stay where I was for ten minutes, after which I could go to the toilet. Of course, you try to think about something else to pass the time, but the controlled clenching tends to dominate your mind and inevitably I was watching the seconds tick by.

I employed a technique I frequently adopt to encourage the passage of time. It involves dividing the period I am enduring in half and marking off that point mentally. Then I divide the remaining time in half again and mark off that point. I keep repeating the process to the end. The great benefit is that each marking off occurs quicker than the one before and there is a flurry of points towards the end that you cannot keep pace with, so that the ending of the event appears to happen all in a rush. It is a technique that saw me safely through many a long hymn as a child and it served me well again lying on this particular hospital bed holding onto excess liquid in a most unnatural way.

I felt quite pleased with myself for being so anally retentive and tried to look casual as I made my way to the toilet to release the torrent. I am pleased to report that I made it with no leakage. Sitting down and relaxing at last there was an impressive flow but unfortunately the process had no impact on the internal blockade.

The medical profession's solution was another enema the following day, and another the day after that, then one the next day. None of them had any impact, despite deeper insertion of the tube each time. Apparently the blockage must have been too far up to reach. Still, it was an interesting and strangely refreshing experience and at least it gave me something to write about.

Although I was decidedly unwell when I arrived for this latest hospital stay, the pains and sickness eased off eventually and towards the end I felt much better. In terms of social interaction it was the most pleasant of my hospital incarcerations. Apart from the first night, I was on a four-bed annex at the end of the ward. It was quiet and none of the residents changed over the five days I was there. This meant that even someone as quiet as me built up a bit of rapport with my fellow inmates. To protect the innocent, I will call them Bill, Bob and Bert.

Bill was the chatty one opposite me; a taxi driver around sixty with a happy demeanour throughout. His cancer had returned and the prognosis was not good but you would never have guessed from the way he kept up a stream of banter. It did not take too many days before you kept hearing some of the stories again, and again, especially as an inevitable eavesdropper on his boisterous conversations with visitors, but you could not help liking him.

Bob was in the bed next to him. He was a large, rough looking guy in his fifties, who told us he had spent time in prison. He had various tattoos, including one on the back of his shaved head. In other contexts he would have been quite intimidating. Lying in bed, suffering with cancer, made him far more approachable. Despite being quite weak, he was allowed out on day release to attend his daughter's wedding. He had all the usual apprehensions as father of the bride, and was worried about his speech, not least because, for medical reasons, he could not drink any alcohol to steady his nerves.

But there was one thing about Bob that exposed his vulnerability more than anything else. He was frightened of needles. None of us liked them but Bob was petrified. At least once a day it was necessary to take blood for tests and it was never straightforward. From the moment he was told it would be happening, Bob could think of nothing else. He would literally weep and groan with dread until the nurses arrived; one to take the blood and the other to try and calm him down. He was never violent, just frightened, shouting out in anticipated fear of the needle's touch. It was an anomalous sight, this hard looking man reduced to tears by a fairly painless routine procedure. I asked him once how he had managed the tattoos. He said it was never a problem because the tattoo needle did not go in deep. It was not pain that he feared, more the needle's penetration. It just shows that we all have our weak points.

The final member of our happy quartet was Bert. Bert was an older man, very weak and scraggy, presumably due to his prolonged cancer but with a full head of dark hair (not necessarily his own). It was never clear how much Bert knew about what was going on. He was always ready with a smile and a quick reply but his hearing was not good and I suspect nodding and saying,

"That's right," was his fall back whenever he missed part of the conversation.

Bert did not appear to have any family but had more visitors than the rest of us put together. His hairdresser and her family came to visit, so did his neighbours and various friends from his previous workplace (he was something to do with motorcycle manufacture). He had obviously been a popular and well known member of the community.

All his conversations were loud because of his hearing problem, so we had no choice but to listen. One of his visitors was greeted with a rather challenging, "Who are you?" and had to explain that he was a former colleague. I felt sorry for him after he had made the effort to visit and then had to justify himself, as if he might be some impostor with evil intent.

One of Bert's neighbours seemed to take responsibility for him and was part of a meeting with a social worker around his bed. They pulled the curtains for privacy but everyone in the room heard the full conversation. It was heartening to see that his neighbours still cared in this day and age. He obviously felt thankful for their support in his old age and frailty.

Another of Bert's visitors was his solicitor and we were all treated to details of his will, in which various sums were allocated from his meagre assets for the benefit of these loyal friends.

As I write this now a year has passed. Since leaving the ward I have no knowledge of what happened to Bill, Bob and Bert. I doubt that they are all still alive. For five days we shared the same living space and the intimacy of common suffering. I never mentioned God and neither did they (despite me bravely having a Bible on my bedside cabinet and even reading it). We never really discussed how we were feeling. We parted with cheerful farewells and good wishes without mentioning our concerns and fears. Even so, I appreciate the fact that our lives brushed together for a time and I remember them with affection.

FROM:	FIONA MAGGS
DATE:	11 OCTOBER 2005
TO:	OUR NETWORK OF FRIENDS AND FAMILY
SUBJECT:	HOME AGAIN

Just to let you all know that Chris has come home this afternoon. He is feeling much better than he was, although his problems are not completely sorted yet. The hope is that we can now cope with things at home but we have to go straight back if any symptoms start again. His trip home is only for a matter of hours though as we are back again tomorrow for the next lot of chemo. The consultant is altering his dose of the drug that he is sensitive to in order to see if they can prevent him being back in hospital next week!

Fiona

JESUS HAS CHEMO

It was my Dad who mentioned it the most. "You ought to write a book about all the funny things that happened to you while you had cancer." He's full of bright ideas. What funny things? I assured him that any account of my journey would not be called, 'The funny side of cancer' or subtitled, 'Amusing anecdotes from the world of oncology'. In fact, I was most insistent that I would not write about it at all. It was a chapter of my life I would be glad to get out of. Documenting it all would involve revisiting the experiences. Yet here I am, writing it all up now. I think there is something primal within some of us, an urge to record and create and tell stories. I lost it when I was so ill but now it is back and I am glad to be myself again. And anyway, my normal life as a pensions consultant is so dull that I'll never get such a good opportunity to make myself sound interesting.

The evening I decided to go ahead and write about my experiences I remember lying in bed and thinking how it would work. There is something special about that moment between being fully awake and being fully asleep. The imagination is unencumbered by reality but still not abandoned to the madness of dreams. I had it all written in my head within a few minutes, and it came out pretty well. If only such thoughts could be transferred to paper automatically, like a computer download.

Instead I had to begin the much more laborious routine of typing word after word, some of them flowing easily and others obstinately refusing to participate. It has made me dwell on the events far longer than I would have done, making it difficult to move on. I want to pick up my life from where it was before cancer struck and part of that involves consciously ignoring the whole episode. I can understand those who say, having gone through some trauma, they just want to forget it. For now I cannot, self-condemned to relive it and convert it all into text.

Every story needs a title and one I have been working with is, 'Jesus has Chemo', which ended up as the title for part one. Hopefully it grabs the attention and prompts the question, "What is that supposed to mean?" It juxtaposes a man who lived two thousand years ago with a modern medical practice; the name of Christ with a terminal illness treatment; the Son of God with hair loss and sickness. It demands explanation.

I have expressed previously how I came to see the actions of others, particularly our Christian friends, as the hand of God at work. Both in prayer and in practical ways they worked with

God, being his 'body' on earth, to support Fiona, me and the children through difficult times. Even within our own family, God was working through each of us to support each other. This recognition of God in others has been like a powerful revelation in developing my perception of God in our world. But it does not end there. I believe God has chosen to work through people but he is not restricted to that alone. He is also with us individually, on a one-to-one basis.

Explaining this concept is difficult. I tried to do it one Sunday morning in our church service around this time. Previously I was actively involved in planning and taking part in our Sunday services. The effects of the tumour, in particular the persistent cough, made it impractical to be up front for several months but now that had eased I wanted to do what I could. I was given a slot each Sunday entitled, 'Chris has had a thought'. It suited me down to the ground as I spent a lot of time thinking and doing little else. The thoughts were not all related to my recent experiences but this particular Sunday I tried to communicate how I felt God had developed a deeper understanding of his presence within me.

I explained that I had always believed God was with us in suffering but my picture of his presence was based on a human perspective. I imagined him primarily as a fellow human coming alongside, offering comfort and sympathy through words, looks and touch, all of which I interpret and understand as care. Or sometimes I imagine God as a bodiless presence, able to plant comforting thoughts directly into my head; a spiritual telepathy. Still, though, this is communication from outside, an external God 'speaking' in his unique way. I do not think these perceptions of God were wrong or unhealthy but at times they felt inadequate. God, it seemed, was always separate from me, offering empathy.

But a deeper experience of God's presence did come. And it came at my lowest points, when emotions had overwhelmed me and logical thought and words were drowned out by feelings. It was here that I felt my soul was exposed. I was totally vulnerable, the illusion of self-control shattered; a naked reality we visit only a handful of times in our lives. It was here that I discovered what God's presence really is. In that terrible and lonely place, stripped of all life's superficial dressings, God was with me in my suffering. The intimacy of his presence was such that I felt we were one. I was not suffering alone, he was suffering with me. He was feeling what I felt, not from outside but from within. It was no longer a terrible and lonely place because he filled it. His presence did not simply support me, it ran through me and strengthened me. I understood the cry echoed in Psalm 23, "Even though I walk through the valley of the shadow of death, I will fear no evil, for you are with me".

My journey sometimes felt like walking through a bleak and dark valley but I was not alone. When I went into hospital, he went into hospital. When I had chemo, he had chemo. I even took to thinking in terms of 'we' rather than 'I' to recognise God's intimate involvement in my suffering. I do not pretend I was always conscious of his presence. I had no holy glow. I was still grumpy and tired. But the certainty of such experiences was deep and powerful and they provided milestones along the path.

Sometimes, as I sat in the chemotherapy unit looking around at all the people there, I wondered how they coped. Most, I guess, had no active Christian faith. All, I am sure, had experienced the same moments of despair as me. Thankfully, for most of us, they do not last long. I suppose people just recover a sense of proportion and get on, allowing day-to-day practicalities to block out the emotional pain.

Except that I believe those rare moments are, in reality, the only true sense of proportion; our tiny human souls facing up to their inadequacy in a vast spiritual universe. It is here that faith in God makes such a difference. As Jesus said, it is like two men building houses. One builds on sand, the other on rock. To the outside world the houses look the same, just as you could not tell which of the chemotherapy patients had faith in God and which were relying on their own inner strength. The difference comes during the heaviest moments of the storm. It was then that I hit the rock of God's firm foundation, and having proved the foundation in one storm I can confidently face the next.

I am sure more troubles will come my way. I do not relish them but I need not fear them either. Death itself holds no sting because I believe God will be with me even through that. It is not a claim I make lightly. I do not pretend to have suffered anything compared to many around the world but, like all of us, I can only judge these things on my own personal experience and I share that honestly with you now. My firm conviction is that God is real and present. Jesus had chemo.

FROM:	FIONA MAGGS
DATE:	26 OCTOBER 2005
TO:	OUR NETWORK OF FRIENDS AND FAMILY
SUBJECT:	ANOTHER INSTALLMENT IN THE EXCITING LIVES OF THE MAGGS!!

Another two weeks have gone by and I have to report that they have been pretty uneventful compared to previous weeks. Chris had his chemo on 12th October and they halved the dose of the drug he is sensitive to (Vinblastin for those who like the technical stuff). With the reduced dose and the continuation of all the drugs to stop his internal paralysis (that is what was happening with the full dose) he has managed to get through the two weeks without any reoccurrence. He did however get a heavy cold which went onto his chest. We acted in good time and got him to the doctors and on antibiotics. This meant that it did not get any more serious because if it had, he would have been back in hospital and on intravenous antibiotics.

Today Chris had the next lot of chemotherapy and we also saw the consultant. She seems to be happy with progress and is arranging another scan to assess the state of the tumour. If there is a better than 50% reduction with the chemo they will then just go onto the radiotherapy (after the 6 months of treatment). If not, they will have to be more aggressive, with more chemo before the radiotherapy.

Chris is coping well with all the treatment although is getting progressively more tired as time goes on. This will continue apparently until after the treatment has stopped.

He went into work again for a couple of hours on Friday although we have now realised that he is not going to be able to get back to doing anything properly until after all the treatment has finished. It looks like it is going to be around a year that he will be off. When Chris went off sick he thought that it may be a couple of weeks and then maybe a month or two. The fatigue lasts for most of the two weeks now and he needs to sleep every day so full time work is a long time off. He hopes to keep visiting work every couple of weeks for a few hours to say hello, catch up on his emails and make sure that his office is as he left it!! The 'Chris has had a thought' slot at church is still continuing and he is managing to come up with his usual level of meaningful, helpful and thought provoking talk. He does spend a lot of time thinking!

Hope that has brought you up to date. Life has settled into the two week pattern now and the rest of life fits around that. Thanks once again for all the messages we get. It is great to hear from you and to know that we are remembered and prayed for.

Thanks, Fiona

FAMILY MATTERS

Reading back through my diary it is full of dull domestic events, normal life flowing relentlessly along beneath the two-weekly chemotherapy cycle. After his disappointing AS level results, Tim was now supposedly studying for his A levels, though opinion differed over the amount of work to be put in. On the 15th of October I wrote, "In the evening I had a man-to-man chat with Tim about work and his lack of effort. Apparently I've got it all wrong and he's just doing enough. The results will tell."

Why is it that teenagers think they know it all? They have been looked after their whole lives, never had experience of life outside of school/college, have virtually no idea how to handle the two most influential factors in our world (sex and money) and generally show a scant disregard for apostrophes. Yet because they can download music to an MP3 player, get through all the levels on the latest extortionately priced computer game and hear the words on singles released by bands I've never heard of, they think it qualifies them to decide:

- how to dress (ripped jeans hanging down below the waistline in the style of a toddler with a soggy nappy);
- what to watch on TV (apparently wholesome family entertainment is 'rubbish' but reality shows featuring

groups of self-absorbed people idling around and swearing for days on end is not); and

- how to spend their time (see above, i.e. downloading music, playing computer games and watching reality TV rather than studying).

I was young once (allegedly) and can vaguely remember the frustration of having parents who didn't understand. But it all seems rather different now. It turns out that parents do know best.

Since Tim was doing IT as one of his A levels, and there is a lot of coursework these days, we settled into the unsatisfactory compromise that if he was sitting at the computer there was a possibility he was working. The fact that the radio was on and messages were flying between him and friends did not necessarily mean he was not concentrating.

Flare-ups took place occasionally, Tim never acknowledging that he ought to work harder. On one occasion before a set of exams, he told us that revision didn't help you get better results. Hmmm. Perhaps we should have dug deeper into what he thought revision was.

To be fair, he did buckle down more when the exams were only a few days away but it was too little too late. The final results, when they arrived in August 2006, were disappointing. At least, they were disappointing to his parents, not least because they fell well short of the level he needed to get his University place. Tim, however, rode them with his typical casual style, still maintaining he had done as well as he expected.

The University agreed to take him anyway, reinforcing his belief that everything works out fine in the end. He had the same attitude towards my cancer, trusting God to sort it all out. I recognise it as faith but I fear it is faith not yet strengthened through testing. The reality is that things will not always work out in Tim's life and as his father I worry about how he will cope when he can't just shrug it off. And I wish he'd pull his trousers up too.

As is often the case, our second son, Luke, is very different. He has a very focussed approach to things (including school work) and gets them done without fuss. As a toddler he was far more demanding then Tim. Negotiating biscuits demonstrated a strong determination at an early age, always pushing for that bit extra. While Tim had amused himself for hours as a toddler, using his creative imagination playing with cars or building things, Luke wanted more attention and was troublesome when he did not get it. So we had some trepidation when he started school that the teachers would find him wearing.

We were amazed at our first parents' evening to discover the opposite. Luke loved the routine of school and the fact that his time was occupied with activity. He will follow instructions happily and prefers being given a task to do rather than having to make his own decisions. He gets on with the job and rarely stops to chat or socialise. It is a teacher's dream characteristic and so we have been greeted with nothing but praise for Luke at every parents' evening since.

Not that everything about Luke is wonderful. His focussed approach means that whenever he has money he feels the need to spend it. When he gets a new computer game he is totally absorbed in it for days until it is mastered. Then it joins the pile of hardly touched oldies.

Every kitchen or garden implement becomes a weapon in Luke's hands, wielded with the skill of a martial arts expert and accompanied by whooshing noises for effect. Empathy is not a strength, although it seems to be developing more recently. As a youngster he seemed to have no understanding of when his siblings had crossed the line from enjoying playful teasing to being upset. He would look on bemused as his sister's laughter turned to hysterical tears and he got the blame.

Luke thinks deeply. So deeply that it is really difficult to bring anything much out of him. His standard response to most questions is, "All right". How was school today? "All right". What did you think of the church service? "All right". How are you feeling about your dad's cancer? "All right". Add to this he shows little emotion and it is difficult to gauge where he is at. Perhaps I ought to worry about him more.

The reason I don't is that I see a lot of myself in Luke. I thought a lot as a youngster, worked through a lot of ideas from the things I saw around me and developed an understanding of God and faith through the people and experiences I had. Little of this was expressed externally but a lot was going on inside. As a result, I had a confidence that I see in Luke too. And now I'm confident that my illness will be another part of life that Luke has absorbed into his database and processed accordingly.

It was a surprise, back in 1995, when our third child turned out to be a girl. If I hadn't been there at the time I wouldn't have believed it. We were so used to boys that the prospect of bringing up a girl was daunting. I recall my first meander down the Barbie aisle of Toys-R-Us. Everything was so pink I felt overwhelmed. But Hannah has brought so much pleasure into our lives and displays many of the typical girlie characteristics. She loves clothes, dolls and cuddly toys. She plans weddings and having a home and children. She has even promised to look after me when I'm old and dribble a lot.

I went shopping with her for Fiona's birthday a few months ago. At ten she knew all the shops to go to, where they were, what they stocked. I just followed along meekly as I have always done with Fiona and many years ago with my mum. The generations pass but shopping remains a closed mystery to me. Left on my own for a moment I feel a faint panic. I have no idea what to do. I just want to go home. It is like the occasion I got lost in a department store when I was a child. I have never felt grown up enough to shop.

Out of our three children, Hannah is the one who has shown most compassion during my illness. When I went into hospital she wrote a note for me to find when I opened my bag. She was the one who wanted to come and visit me there and made a card to bring with her. It is part of her nature to express her love with hugs and kisses, keen to display feelings that the boys are a little embarrassed to admit to. Equally, Hannah managed to come out with the most hurtful comments, her wicked sense of humour overstepping the mark more than once.

I prayed with Hannah most nights as I put her to bed. We prayed about my cancer often during those months. Thinking about what to pray and talking it over with her in a simple way was an opportunity for me to think things through myself. We did not pray for instant healing as I was sure God had already said that would not happen. We prayed instead that I would be strong and faithful through the journey. I hope those moments of prayer meant as much to her as they did to me.

Before we had children we thought it very important to treat any offspring equally. We still do, in theory, but now we realise how very difficult that is when they do not oblige by being equal themselves. Each has their own strengths and weaknesses and you cannot help but compare them. When I was in hospital I read a book called, 'Bringing home the prodigals' by Rob Parsons. It encouraged parents to find time to think about the things they loved about their children and tell them. I wrote down my thoughts while in hospital and, over the first couple of days after I got home, I spent a few minutes alone which each of them to say what I'd written. It was a simple exercise but well worth doing. I will not embarrass them further by recording it all here.

I have sometimes wondered what I would have done if my cancer had spread and I knew that an early death was imminent. How would I say goodbye? What words would I like to leave behind for my children? In my day dreaming I imagined writing letters to be opened by each of them at critical moments in their lives; reaching eighteen or twenty-one, getting married, having a child.

I pictured the scene, a silent tear welling up in their eye as dad spoke wisdom to them from the grave. In a sense it would be easier to say some things that way than in the flesh. Life passes along so quickly we rarely take each other aside to express the things that really matter. I suspect it is only in soaps and TV dramas that parents and children routinely have such heart-to-heart discussions. While I have the opportunity to spend time with them, I pray that I will remember how much family matters.

FROM:	**FIONA MAGGS**
DATE:	**19 NOVEMBER 2005**
TO:	**OUR NETWORK OF FRIENDS AND FAMILY**
SUBJECT:	**SCAN NEWS**

Just thought that I had better let you all know that we now have a date for the next scan. It is on Wednesday morning at 9.40am at the Coventry and Warwick hospital in Coventry. We then have a clinic appointment at 1.30pm at the Walsgrave hospital and then chemotherapy at around 2.00pm (or whenever we get out of clinic). It is going to be a very busy day with plenty of travelling around. We will not have any results I expect for a couple of weeks at least.

Chris has been doing OK over the last few weeks. He has had a problem with his eyes and is on antibiotic eye drops but apart from that we are managing all the side effects with a cocktail of drugs. He is very tired and sleeping most days but is in good spirits and now taking on more responsibility at church, planning and leading the first part of Sunday morning services. Last week he did a sketch with Tim which went well although his voice is still a little rough!

Please continue to pray for us. The chemotherapy treatment is now half way through. Chris is finding that he dislikes it more as time goes on. The veins in his arms are starting to harden due to the drugs and so please pray that we will not have any problems with them not being able to find a suitable vein. There is a particular smell on the unit which Chris seems to notice strongly and also dislikes.

Thank you for remembering us and caring.
Fiona

LOOSE ENDS

It is difficult to capture the tedium of life during chemotherapy. It was not dramatically bad. That would, at least, have been something to write about. It was just dull. I slept most days and the rest of the time was a heady blur of cross-stitch, watching TV and sitting staring into space (a bit like watching TV but without the pictures or sound). Actually, I found a lot of peace in simply sitting and gazing at nothing in particular. It would be nice to claim I was meditating or deep in prayer but I wasn't. I was often just doing nothing - and enjoying it. My head was fuddled by the chemo drugs and my body was tired. I wasn't a vegetable but maybe I learnt a little about the tranquillity of plant life. It was very relaxing.

I once did some psychological tests as part of a course at work. They identified me as a certain type and I got a printout of my supposed typical characteristics. I remember it said that, under stress, I was likely to retract into myself and take to watching reruns of old programmes I'd seen in younger days. It struck me as an odd thing to say at the time but, sure enough, I found myself greatly enjoying watching 'Ever Decreasing Circles', a sitcom from the eighties. I now have all four series on DVD and would happily watch them end-to-end if allowed.

Amongst this monotony, odd moments stand out. One evening in October as I was getting ready for bed I noticed a small black spot on my abdomen. It was where one of my drains had been, now marked by a criss-cross scar left by a stitch long removed. I picked at it and it seemed hard so I asked Fiona what she thought. She poked and prodded, decided there was something in there, then went for the tweezers. In our house Fiona is always the one who goes for the tweezers. She admits to actually enjoying pulling out splinters and the like, which is more than can be said for the rest of us who are enduring the pain.

After a little work she managed to get hold of it and gently pulled. Slowly a piece of thread emerged. It was a strange sensation watching her draw it gradually out. It did not hurt and the area was not at all sore but I could sense it pulling as it left me. After a centimetre or so the thread broke, leaving another small piece hanging out. Fiona was enjoying the challenge and set to work again. This time it was harder work but she persisted and was rewarded by another centimetre's worth. It seemed odd to me that this bit of debris had been sitting in my body for three months, making its way to the surface without any fuss.

The body is a remarkable organism and its ability to deal with invasive material and heal itself is phenomenal. My chest bone was laced back together with stainless steel wire when my operation was finished, no doubt a remarkably skilled process in itself. But this was merely to hold things in place while my body did the really clever stuff in grafting the bone together again over several weeks. It is rare that we stop and think about our bodies much. We take them for granted until something goes wrong.

There is a psalm (number 139) in the Bible that ponders the wonder of our bodies and concludes we are "fearfully and wonderfully made". Interesting that 'fear' should come into it but I suppose there is that sense that when we have cause to consider what are bodies are up to (behind our backs, if that's possible) we realise again we are not so much in control of our bodies as we thought. And if, like me, you recognise the hand of God in the process you get a little more perspective on our relative capabilities.

About a week after the incident with the thread, our friends Aaron and Diane returned from their six-month stint in America. Diane called us to see how things were but Fiona was out and I was dozing in bed. I answered the phone drowsily but was pleased to hear her cheerful voice. She asked about the chemo and how I was coping. Then, out of the blue, I heard, "And what about the sex?" "Well," I thought, "Diane's back and she's asking some pretty direct questions!" Incredulous, I repeated the question back to her. It turned out I'd misheard. What she'd actually said was, "What about the effects?" as in the side-effects of the chemo. I don't know which of us was the more embarrassed.

Other highlights included the odd trip into my workplace. I was in no condition to do any work but it was well worth popping in to chat to a few people and sit at my desk for a while. The first time I did this I felt very self-conscious, aware that I looked a shadow of my former self. But the effort was worthwhile in terms of keeping in touch with what was going on and reminding them that I would be coming back!

I might have joked that I was making sure nobody had taken over my desk, except that for a month or so someone did. A sister company had a flooding problem and had to operate from our building for a while. Apparently four people were working from my desk during this period. But when I went in it was much as I'd left it; the same piles of non-urgent papers sitting there, ever hopeful I would one day get around to doing something with them. It was an opportunity to throw away lots of clutter, the sort of cleansing I never had time for when working; my text books from studying for professional exams twenty years ago, materials from courses I went on and never looked at again, expenses sheets since the beginning of time, they all found their way into the bin.

Luke got his first detention at school during this period too. Like all parents we took great pride in his first smile, his first words, his first steps and so on. We could not help taking a little pleasure at the latest 'first' he had achieved, especially given the circumstances.

In a French lesson the class had been told to write a description of their teacher. Luke did so rather too literally, not drawing back on the negatives. The teacher took it in good spirit at the time but the next day he said he had reflected on it and decided that Luke had been disrespectful. He gave Luke a pink slip (three pink slips leading to a detention) and that seemed to be the end of it. Over a week later another member of staff, with some sort of behavioural management role, told Luke he had heard about what had happened and was giving him a detention! Fiona was incensed at the injustice of it all and wanted to contact the school. Luke persuaded her not to, an indignant parent apparently being a great source of embarrassment to a young man these days.

So she let it go and Luke duly arrived at this member of staff's room to serve his detention on the appointed day. He was not there. Luke waited for twenty minutes and even asked other staff if they knew where he was. Nobody did. So Luke came home. The next day Luke went to find him to explain what had happened. The member of staff had obviously forgotten about the detention but made no apology. He just told Luke that he hoped he had learned his lesson and the matter was closed. I think Luke did learn a few lessons from the incident, though perhaps not the ones the school would have wanted him to.

FROM:	FIONA MAGGS
DATE:	1 DECEMBER 2005
TO:	OUR NETWORK OF FRIENDS AND FAMILY
SUBJECT:	ANOTHER UPDATE ON CHRIS

Last week went OK although there was some difficulty getting a needle into Chris's arm when he went for his scan (six attempts). We should get the results next Wednesday (7th Dec) when we have an extra appointment with the Consultant before chemo.

Because of the problems that he has been having with getting access to a vein we have decided to have a permanent line fitted called a picc line. This is going to be fitted next Tuesday at 10.00am and involves having a thin tube going in through his arm (below the elbow) and along the vein into his body. It will end just above his heart (the superior vena cava - again for the more technically minded) and sit in place for the rest of the treatment. All the rest of his drugs can be given through this line and also they should be able to take blood from it as well. He will be x-rayed to check it is in the right place and then he will need to have it flushed (stuff put through it to make sure that it does not get blocked) every week.

Chris is feeling a little anxious about this. Please pray that everything will go according to plan.

Thanks yet again for all your prayers and concerns.
Fiona

OTHER FAMILY MATTERS

It would be difficult to overestimate how important our church 'family' is to us. Some people may find that surprising, if their experience of church is negative, or at best indifferent. I would suggest that such people have only met with religion and not really experienced church at all. Church is not a building or services on Sundays, it is a community of people trying to live out their faith together. They care about each other, support each other, look out for each other, encourage each other, love each other. Okay, they are not perfect. In fact, one of the main qualifications on the Christian journey of faith is an acceptance of your own failings. But they are committed to each other under the common banner of God's grace and forgiveness.

We have experienced this 'other family' throughout our lives and it is so integral to the way we live I cannot imagine being outside of it. Much of our time and energy is spent in church activities and our social lives revolve around it too. It focuses our spiritual purpose and provides opportunities to develop our gifts as well as be helped by others. Like all families there are sometimes frustrations to work through and difficulties to be overcome but, in our experience, it is a truly good network and I thank God for it.

Our church met in Dickens Heath. The area was mainly fields ten years ago, with the odd rural dwelling scattered here and there. Somebody had the idea of developing it into a village to provide much needed housing for Solihull. The plan was that there would be a green with a cricket pitch, a country pub and, of course, a church.

Ten years later the reality is as far from a village as you can imagine. There is a green, originally designed for cricket but now encroached upon by so many buildings that a six would be sure to break someone's window. I have never seen anybody playing cricket on it, though there is a sign by the children's play area thoughtfully pointing out that children are more at risk during a cricket match. There is a pub too, not next to the green but around the corner in the designer label High Street. Actually, it is more of a wine bar to cater for the young upwardly mobile business people who can afford the expensive houses and apartments.

And there is a church. Not, as the planners originally envisaged, an old English church building with a spire and a regular stream of weekend weddings, but a family of believers meeting in the community school and trying to live God's kingdom values in a sprawl of continuing building development. The latest phase is a square of waterfront apartments (there being a nearby canal) four stories high and somewhat exclusive in price.

We got involved in planting a church there over four years ago. It was not easy to move away from the church that had been our home and family for the previous fifteen years but we believe God led us into something new and we have grown immensely through it all.

There are some great stories of churches in deprived areas making a real difference to the community around them. Dickens Heath was never going to be that sort of story but, the way I see it, rich people need God too! Jesus once said it was easier for a camel to go through the eye of a needle than for a rich man to enter the kingdom of heaven. His disciples found these sort of statements baffling but Jesus often said puzzling things and invited people to engage in some challenging thinking.

I believe there is a spiritual battle to be undertaken against the materialism of our culture and our church's job is to fight it on the avenues and closes of Dickens Heath. The secure gated apartment blocks we cannot access, even to post publicity leaflets, are representative of a sub-culture that wants to cut itself off from the rest of society. A large part of our work in the village has been to encourage a sense of community, including open-air concerts and running community based Easter and Christmas activities but there is still a lot more to do.

And of course we do not always get it right. I reckon we could have claimed the national award for the most ineffective carol singing event of 2005. It took place on a bitterly cold windy Saturday morning. The church turnout was poor. I think there were five of us at most and no instruments. We were set up, for some obscure reason, outside the library, just away from the High Street, where there was virtually no passing traffic.

Occasionally someone would scuttle past to return their library books and give us a sympathetic smile. One lady even stopped and sang with us for a short while, hoping perhaps to swell our weary voices beyond the two metre range we were managing before the wind whipped our warbling strains away.

We had a table, on which were an optimistic pile of carol sheets. At least these provided some amusement for distant onlookers when they blew away and we chased them down the road. And the manager of the Village Hall kindly brought us some warm food and mulled wine, which he balanced precariously on the wind-swept table. We all eyed it cautiously as we battled bravely through endless verses of 'While Shepherds Watched', fearful that an extra gust would topple the whole lot. It was not a vision of the church triumphant.

Starting a church up from scratch presents lots of challenges in terms of how things are done. The start-up group came from different church backgrounds so there was no obvious tradition to fall back on. We did not even decide on our denominational allegiance for over a year, eventually spreading ourselves over two. The process between made us think hard about what we believed were truly fundamental principles, in order to distinguish them from what we had to admit were merely personal preferences. It could have been the cause of many disagreements among us but in fact it was really encouraging. We felt that God guided us into a unity of thought as we humbled ourselves to listen to each other and his Spirit.

For me, one of the best aspects of the new church was that both Fiona and I were part of the leadership team. Previously I have had church leadership roles but Fiona has not. This time we were able to serve together and it was a tremendous experience. Fiona's gifts are very different to mine and it was great to see them recognised and fully used.

This period of sharing in leadership finished at the end of 2005 after four years, though the last year was disrupted by my health. We formed some very close friendships with our fellow leaders and their support was very evident when I was ill. As a leadership team they decided to fast and pray for me every time I had chemo. It was a commitment they probably regretted having taken on at times, as the chemo dragged out over six months, but it meant a lot to me.

It was hard leaving the leadership team for both of us. The role involves spending a lot of 'quality time' with people, talking through things that really matter at many levels. Losing that intimacy meant falling back in terms of relationships as well as losing touch with the detail of what was going on. Fiona felt this more keenly. In a sense I was more willing to let go as I did not feel well enough to give it the attention it needed. We have learnt a lot from coming off the leadership too though and it is good to see things from both sides of the fence.

We took responsibility for organising our church's children's Christmas presentation this year. In fact, it sometimes feels like we've taken responsibility for the children's Christmas presentation every year since I can remember. It gets increasingly difficult to come up with a new angle. This year we followed the current TV fad for competitions where there are a large number of contestants to start with and they gradually get whittled down.

The big casting problem for the nativity is, of course, Mary. All the girls want the part. Joseph is much less problematic. Here the difficulty is finding a boy happy to hold hands with a girl! And boys have plenty of other options; the splendour of the wise men/kings for those who like dressing up or the scruffy looking shepherds for the more 'outdoor type'. The girls who don't make Mary usually end up in the chorus line as angels.

So we started auditions for Mary in the Sunday service three weeks before the event, under the heading, 'Something About

Mary'. There were eight girls who wanted the part so we got them to try on the obligatory blue headscarf and they all looked suitably sweet and innocent as we talked about who Mary was. I did not have the nerve to tell anyone they were out of the competition.

The following Sunday was a little more demanding as we looked at the song Mary sang when she visited her cousin Elizabeth and each of them had to sing a bit. We managed to get it down to six simply because two pulled out voluntarily, not wishing to sing up front, but I started to realise I had not really thought this through. There was only one week left and someone had to decide, in front of the whole congregation, who would be Mary; which meant telling five disappointed girls, in front of their adoring parents, they were not! How could it be done? I even toyed with the idea of letting them all do it, though how Joseph would cope with a whole flock of Marys was hard to imagine, and it would leave the angelic host noticeably thin on the ground.

Only five of the potential six turned up on the penultimate Sunday but all were still eager to take the role. We looked at the part of the story where Mary and Joseph arrive in Bethlehem. I asked four people to act as Innkeepers at the four corners of the school hall and got each Mary to choose a Joseph and a donkey from the remaining congregation (adults included). Then they all had to run from inn to inn asking if there was room for them to stay. One of the Innkeepers had instructions to say he had a stable, after being asked a set number of times, and by that rather complicated means we selected our Mary (and, by default, her Joseph). I could claim some biblical precedent related to drawing lots but, to be honest, it was a cop out to avoid me having to choose between them.

The following Sunday we did the whole story in our Christmas service, our daughter Hannah doing a great job as the narrator. The rest was all improvised by the kids. Somehow they managed to split into two extreme schools of acting; one being the minimalist inanimate style in which they appear to have no idea what is going on and the other involving gross over acting. As one of the parents said, "A little bit of balance would be a good thing but never mind".

As usual, I pledged to myself never to arrange the Christmas nativity again. But a year is a long time in which to forget.

FROM: **FIONA MAGGS**
DATE: **21 DECEMBER 2005**
TO: **OUR NETWORK OF FRIENDS AND FAMILY**
SUBJECT: **MORE PROBLEMS!!**

Another update on Chris for you all.

Yesterday when Chris went for his blood test the nurse discovered that he had a blood clot in his right arm. He had had a clot in his picc line last week which they had managed to clear. This new clot is not in the line but in his arm which is swollen and discoloured. They put him onto some daily injections of heparin.

Today we saw our Oncology consultant and the bad news was that they decided to remove the picc line. This is a little frustrating to Chris as it has only been used once for his chemo and has involved lots of extra hospital visits and it was not easy to get in, in the first place. He has now been referred to the anticoagulant clinic and we have an appointment on Friday morning as they want to start him on warfarin before Christmas. This will again mean lots of extra visits and blood tests as they have to get the dose right. The chemo had to be given in his other arm - that went very well and the nurse got the cannula in straight away. He does now have a sore and painful right arm. Hopefully they will be able to give him the next three doses of chemo OK although if there is a problem they will have to consider something else.

We look forward to a quiet Christmas (Chris will be sleeping off the effects of his chemo) and hope that you will all have an enjoyable and Christ centred Christmas.

With love,
Fiona (and Chris)

WORKING THE PICC LINE

It was all supposed to make things easier. A permanent picc line in my arm would avoid the need for them to insert needles in me for blood tests (fortnightly) and chemo (again fortnightly). With all the difficulties they were having getting the needles in due to my veins hardening it seemed the best solution. If only life would oblige by working out as simply as we intend.

We travelled to Coventry one Tuesday for a 10 a.m. appointment on the ward where I have my chemo. We met the nurse trained to do picc lines. It's a procedure doctors always used to do but the progressive thinking is that it's the sort of job that can now be done by specialist nurses. I think it's a good thing, both for the nurses who take on more challenging roles and the patients who benefit from having a specialist on the job. Except, of course, you don't become a specialist overnight and there is a learning curve to ascend. I suspect I was part of that learning curve.

First the nurse applied some local anaesthetic cream to one arm, and then the other, just in case. The anaesthetic took an hour to work and made my arms feel very cold. During the wait she did a blood test and explained the procedure. As usual I did not take in the detail but I do recall mention of a larger needle being necessary. I was also 'measured up' for the length of tubing to be inserted.

It was around 11.30 a.m. before the anaesthetic had done its job and I was invited to get onto the bed. It was the only bed in the room, all the other patients sitting in chairs to have their treatment. It marked me out as special, a little bit of one-upmanship suggesting my ordeal was going to be worse than theirs today. There was a good deal of preparation, getting all the right equipment ready, then the curtains were drawn around. It is a quaint touch. There's something decidedly British about the modesty of those thin curtains drawing a discreet veil around anything unseemly.

First, my nurse tried inserting the needle into a vein in my left arm but there was an obstruction. Then she tried a second vein but it bruised straight away. A third vein was identified and the 53cm of tubing was nearly all inserted before hitting a blockage. After poking it around a little she had to admit defeat and withdraw it.

Suitable veins having been exhausted on my left she moved herself and her equipment around to the other side. I was beginning to lose confidence (I only had two arms) and resorted to prayer. Thankfully the first vein on my right arm was successful and the tube was fully inserted. Even so, there was a lot of blood oozing out. It was actually a pleasant sensation to feel its warmth seeping over my cold arm. Strange how bleeding can be so nice. Unfortunately I bled on the bed, on the curtains, on the floor and on the nurse's shoes too. I found myself apologising, taking responsibility for the contents of my body now spilled liberally abroad.

Once the tube was inserted I had to go over to the X-ray Department to check it was in the right place. They fitted us in quickly and the X-ray confirmed all was as it should be, except for a minor adjustment (pulling it out by 1 cm). The cannula at the entry point was firmly capped and taped down and I was free to leave, now the proud owner of half a meter of additional internal tubing. We made our way to Burger King for lunch, partly for the cuisine and partly because they had a bountiful supply of free golden crowns made from card. We requisitioned three of them for the wise men in our church nativity!

For a while afterwards, I had to put a heat pad on my arm four times a day and wear some tubigrip at night to stop the cannula catching but otherwise my new body component did not prevent me from doing much. (I couldn't play the violin but I suspect that's because I never learnt.) I was very conscious of the cannula at first but soon got used to it. The day after it was fitted I returned for chemo and had the best session ever. No needles to insert and no sensation in my arm as the tubing took the chemo right into my chest. There was a small amount of bleeding from the entry point occasionally over the next few days, which took us back to the hospital to check everything was okay, but they said it was fine.

A week later my picc line was due for its first flush. This meant another trip to a more local hospital. Their day ward for chemo patients was much smaller but similarly decked out with high backed chairs spaced around the room. Beyond was a large lounge area in the style of a conservatory. Friends and relatives could come here and relax by reading pamphlets on cancer!

I was sent to wait in the conservatory when I first arrived. It was nice and quiet, no day-time TV babbling in the background. Sitting there on my own, waiting to be seen, I just stared into space and found it very peaceful. As soon as another man came in though the atmosphere changed. Neither of us said anything beyond a courteous grunt of greeting. He picked up a magazine and settled down to read it but somehow the presence of another person broke my sense of peacefulness. It did not feel right to just sit and stare into space anymore. The potential for social interaction created a tension. I felt as if I should say something, start a conversation maybe. I had no idea what to say. "Got cancer?" seemed a little abrupt. I shut my eyes and ignored him instead.

Soon I was called back into the ward for treatment. Unfortunately, the flushing process proved problematic. It involved injecting some saline solution through the line to check it was clear but there seemed to be a blockage and nothing was moving. The nurse tried several times and even called the hospital in Coventry for advice but it was still not working. As I had done when there were problems getting the picc line fitted, I shot off a prayer in my mind. As I did so the nurse tried flushing the line for a final time and it worked. Coincidence? I don't think so.

I confess I am not a person who prays with great faith. I bring my requests to God a little awkwardly, expecting I'm not quite on the mark and that the answer to the problem I'm bringing is likely to be resolved in mysterious ways I will never quite grasp. I probably think too much and pray too little. On these two occasions, though, I prayed more out of desperation than intellect. Maybe that is why God responded so readily. I am not suggesting desperation is a magic formula by any means. I know many people have prayed in desperation and not got their request granted. Even so, I am sure the heart prays louder than the brain.

I had another flush process a few days later and it all went fine. Then, just two weeks after having the picc line fitted, I went for a regular blood test. I wondered whether to mention the few burst blood vessels at the top of my arm. After all, I had several burst blood vessels on my chest still and nobody seemed worried about them. I casually threw it into conversation and they had a look. "Oh, yes my armpit is a bit tender now you mention it," I admitted. And when they compared my two arms and hands side by side one did seem a little swollen and discoloured. Funny how you don't notice these things yourself. It all added up to a clot in my arm; not in the picc line itself but outside it. The clot was blocking the flow of blood, making it try and force through smaller vessels to find another way around and bursting these smaller vessels in the process.

An ultra-sound confirmed the diagnosis. The operator was keen to show me the image on screen. She said the 'gungy-stuff' (her own technical term) was the clot. I looked at the area she was pointing at and smiled as if I was a parent-to-be seeing my unborn child for the first time. It seemed to be what she wanted.

They started me on daily injections to thin my blood. More needles. It was a cruel twist given that the whole point (excuse the pun) of the picc line was to reduce the perforations.

The following day, when I was due to have chemo again, they removed the picc line. I had hoped that they could at least use it to give me the chemo first but apparently it was too risky. So it came out and yet another needle went in. And to make matters worse I had to go onto Warfarin tablets to reduce the risk of clotting for the next six months, requiring many additional blood tests to check the levels. The picc line had served its purpose for only one chemo session but, in the end, resulted in six additional trips to hospital, twenty-seven extra blood tests, fifteen self-injections and 730 Warfarin tablets.

The specialist nurse assured me this had never happened to one of her patients before (as if that somehow made it better) so I would not want to put anyone off the idea. It would have been a great help if it had worked out as intended. But, for me, the journey just got diverted through one of God's mysterious ways.

FROM:	**FIONA MAGGS**
DATE:	**20 JANUARY 2006**
TO:	**OUR NETWORK OF FRIENDS AND FAMILY**
SUBJECT:	**UPDATE ON CHRIS**

Thought it was time to get in touch again and let you all know what is happening in the Maggs household. Not a lot really, which I suppose is good news.

Chris has been stabilised on his Warfarin (for the blood clot) and the daily blood tests have now been reduced to a weekly test. The end is in sight now for the chemotherapy. He had chemo on Wednesday and that went very smoothly. The nurse got the cannula in first time and the treatment was given without any problems. The main difficulty at the moment seems to be that Chris is extremely tired most of the time. At the beginning of treatment he would spend the first few days after chemo sleeping during the day but then would have days when he was not too bad and did not need to sleep in the day. Now he needs to sleep every day and seems to be able to do less.

This week we celebrated one year since Chris first went to the doctors because he was unwell. He had been feeling rough for some time before he got round to going! Actually, we celebrated with the 11th dose of chemo! The next lot is the last lot. We have an appointment on the day before (31st Jan) to see the Consultant that is going to take Chris over and sort out the radiotherapy and then follow him up in the future. We are not sure when the radiotherapy will start but it will be after the 15th February (that is day 28 of his chemotherapy treatment - the drugs are given on day 1 and 15).

What else is happening in the house? Tim has been on 2 weeks exam leave. He only went back to school for 2 days following the Christmas holidays and then got study leave. Today he took his first A level paper and has another on Tuesday. The rest of the exams are in June and then we wait for the results! He now has two interviews at University and has been offered a place on the course that was his last choice and he is not really interested in! He has not yet heard from his first choice at Portsmouth.

I think that is all to tell you at the moment. Time does seem to go by quickly (it does for me, sometimes it is slower for Chris). He has now been off work 8 months and although we have no idea when he will be well enough to go back the subject keeps cropping up in different ways. It is going to be quite a challenge getting back and there may be a change of role for him within the company although nothing has been discussed. Please pray for us that the work situation will be well planned and Chris will end up in just the right place.

Thank you for your love, care and prayers.
Many thanks
Fiona

GRUMPY OLD MAN

One of the accusations frequently levelled at me by my family during chemo, and not without justification, was that I was grumpy. Some of that must be down to the treatment but I like to think that underneath my pleasant persona lurks a grumpy old man waiting to get out. Illness just speeded up the process. So, accepting this affliction with grace, I thought I'd make the most of the opportunity and record the sort of things that get me going; things that get up my nose and start me ranting. In no particular order....

Christmas shopping.

I don't mind the exchanging of gifts at Christmas. In fact, I think it's a good idea, making us think about other people instead of ourselves at least once a year. The trouble is, I'm no good at it. Fiona writes out lists of people and starts filling it with ideas months ahead. She invites my participation but anything I say is instantly dismissed – not appropriate, too expensive, not expensive enough, might already have one, we gave them that last year, they might not even like sushi; the list seems endless.

I leave her to it but still the insane idea that I might come up with 'just the thing' lingers in my head. Which is why I popped into a local garden centre in December, on the way back from some errand. It was one of those garden centres that has expanded into a wide range of ornaments, crafts, games, novelty items and so on, the ideal place to pick up one or two unique gifts.

My confidence began to wane as soon as I entered the premises. Where to look first? I made for the games area and stood for ages, contemplating the range of amusements on offer. It is at this point that I realised I had virtually no idea what people would like and even less inclination to buy things at the prices charged. I came away with nothing, except a sense of despondency and a renewed respect for Fiona's ability to deliver the goods year on year.

Sticky plasters

I had more plasters and sticky tape applied to my body during my cancer treatment than a Blue Peter creation. Most of them were applied liberally to secure a cannula or the like in place. Of course you want it to be firm, but every piece applied had to be removed, usually taking with it several of those small hairs that seem to serve no purpose other than inflicting pain when plucked from your body.

Why is it that in these modern technologically advanced days nobody has come up with a plaster that leaves those hairs alone? I even asked if they could shave the area of my arms that took the regular punishment. Apparently not, as a nick in the skin could lead to infection. Instead the hairs were yanked out individually over the months, every one of them kicking and screaming.

The nurses were not unsympathetic to my plight. But the slower and more careful they tried to be the more it hurt. In the end I had to admit the 'quick rip' approach was best; one of those examples of being cruel to be kind.

Waiting on the telephone

Although a proportion of my salary was covered through my employer by an income protection scheme, I did have to claim Incapacity Benefit after six months of being off work to top up our income. This was a cumbersome and bureaucratic process as you would expect but it was not helped by the difficulty of getting in touch with the people dealing with it. These days such claims are administered through Job Centre Plus offices, or 'jobcentreplus' as their logo would have it, someone no doubt under the illusion that omitting capital letters and spaces makes them more modern and approachable.

If they want to be approachable they might try answering their telephones! To quote from their correspondence, "If you want to ask us anything about this letter, please get in touch with us. Our phone number and address are at the top of this letter." The phone rang and rang and rang. I gave up. I tried again later. No reply. And later. This time it was answered fairly quickly and I explained what I wanted to talk about. "Sorry, the people who deal with Incapacity Benefit go home at half past four."

I tried the next day and persisted until the phone was answered. This time I was asked to wait while they put me through to someone. Classical music was played for my entertainment, the least they could do since I was now paying for the call. It was a well-known section of a piece I recognised. It was an even more well-known section by the time I had heard it forty times over. I was sick of it after waiting on hold for twenty minutes and calculating that this call had cost much more than the price of the stamp I was attempting to save (and would now have to use anyway).

I gave up and put the phone down. Still, at least music is better than those lines with a regularly repeated reassurance that you are a valued customer, each repetition seemingly tinged with a little more sarcasm than the one before.

Radio phone-ins

Spending so much more time at home increased the amount of radio I listened to. Generally I'm happy with easy-listening music and banal banter but I do get wound up by the phone-ins. It's not the topics that get to me, it's just the pointlessness of the whole thing.

For example, I listened to one on boarding schools; are they good or bad? One person called to say she went to boarding school and hated it. The next called to say he went to boarding school and enjoyed it immensely. Then someone rang in to say he never went to boarding school but wished he had, followed by another caller saying her niece went to a boarding school but went on to fail her degree course (as if that were proof enough that the whole boarding school system should be scrapped with immediate effect).

And so it goes on and on and on, one person after another giving their individual opinion or experience. And where does it lead? Nowhere. There is no conclusion, no summary, no attempt to validate or challenge, no analysis, no point whatsoever. It is just cheap 'entertainment' disguised as a serious programme.

And it is worse when the subject is something that really matters. Somehow the airing of uninformed views, the more extreme the better as far as the show is concerned, is passed off as debate.

And while I'm on the subject, why do so many shows on TV and the radio invite public participation? I like to watch or listen to be entertained. I don't want to join in! The prime example of this in recent years is the 'talent' show. The format usually consists of a panel of experts, all suitably qualified to make sensible judgments in their specialist areas, so let them decide who goes through to next week. Why put the burden on my shoulders? I have enough to worry about in my life. I tune in for a bit of relaxation and suddenly find the future career of some desperate youngsters thrust into my hands. It's all too much!

I could go on; I usually do. Anyway, at least I've given you a flavour of things people are best to avoid raising with me, unless they want to see the grumpy old man emerge.

FROM:	FIONA MAGGS
DATE:	2 FEBRUARY 2006
TO:	OUR NETWORK OF FRIENDS AND FAMILY
SUBJECT:	NO MORE CHEMO!

Another mile stone reached. Chris had his last chemo on Wednesday afternoon and although he actually felt quite ill afterwards he was really pleased to get that finished. He now has a few days of sleeping that off and starting to make some recovery.

On Tuesday we saw the new Consultant who is going to sort out the next part of the treatment. He was very helpful and spent some time explaining the treatment and talking us through the implications. The radiotherapy seems to be more extensive than Chris or I had initially realised. They will be radiating a large area of his chest, going right up to the lower part of his neck. He will be blasted from the front and back. The implications of this are that anything in the way will also be affected. This means that part of both his lungs, his throat and the edge of his heart will be in the line of fire. There will be permanent scarring and possible narrowing of the throat. During treatment his throat will be sore and he may have some difficulty eating (especially spicy foods or coke!).

Before all this can happen Chris has to have a series of tests to make sure that they radiate everything that is left after the chemo. Once he has had the radiotherapy they will not treat the same area again, so the first time is the only chance! He will now have another CT scan and they may follow this with a PET scan (shows up areas of cell activity) if needed. They will also do some lung function tests. We get a month or so off following the chemo (filled with tests!) so expect the radiotherapy to start some time in March.

One thing that the Consultant did was show us all the scan pictures. We have been waiting to see them since the September ones were taken. He showed us May, September and November pictures. One thing that we were surprised about was that in November although the tumour had shrunk, it was not by as much as we had imagined. There was still quite a chunk there and it was also pretty big in the first place - a lot to get rid of.

Although everything is heading in the right direction there is still some way to go. We came away from the consultation on Tuesday realising that we had perhaps begun to simplify the situation and forgotten the seriousness of what still lay ahead. Despite this we still have a strong confidence in the power of God and his constant love and support throughout everything. There may be many more things to face yet but we are both still positive.

It has been a busy week with hospital appointments. Chris is still on the Warfarin for his blood clot and he last week developed another complication. He had an infection/abscess under one of his fingernails.

The chemo has slowly destroyed his fingernails and this one had got very painful and although he started antibiotics ended up in A&E. There they removed his fingernail (under local anaesthetic) cleaned up the gunk from the infection, and put the fingernail back. He was in a sling for a day with a dressing on the finger a few times bigger than the finger!! This has meant that we now pay visits to the Orthopaedic surgeon at Alexandra Hospital, Redditch. Chris is also having at least weekly blood tests for the Warfarin levels although this week it has been three blood tests. We have been somewhere every day this week, 2 times to Coventry, 2 times to Redditch and once to the GP. He hasn't got time to go to work!

Well, I think that is enough for now. As you can see it has been quite an eventful two weeks. We are hoping for a quieter few weeks now with less appointments. Thank you to everyone who sends back a word of encouragement. It is good to know that the emails do reach you.

With love, Fiona

I FEEL IT IN MY FINGERS

Ever since I started chemo the doctors looked at my fingernails when doing their check-ups. At first I did not know what they were looking for. Everything seemed fine. But after a couple of months marks started to appear on the skin underneath and gradually healthy nail beds turned into unsightly, dull-yellow, blotchy ones. It is the soft tissues that get affected by chemo most and the fingernail beds are an easily identifiable measure of how things are going. I guess it is an indicator that the chemo is working and the doctors may have been pleased to see the signs.

Like the hair loss, having mangy fingernails was an outward appearance of my illness, or more correctly an outward appearance of my treatment. I was not particularly self-conscious about it but in the right circumstances it could be used to elicit a little sympathy. The gunk that developed under the nails was a bit smelly, though I only really noticed that when attempting to pick my nose. The area was tender too, so drumming my fingernails on a table would hurt. And I could no longer open certain types of packaging – flip-up tops on shower gel and milk cartons for instance. I could get other people to help with the milk cartons and I managed without drumming my fingers but the nose thing was a little inconvenient.

Then in the evening of 22nd January I noticed the skin under the nail of the fourth finger on my left hand was tender and slightly swollen. It got worse during the night, making sleep difficult. By the morning it was throbbing and a bright yellow patch had developed, contrasting with the dull yellow of the rest of the nail bed. A trip to the doctor's got me onto antibiotics but the bright yellow patch spread quickly and filled the nail, making it very tender to touch. In fact, the whole finger was swollen. Fortunately I had removed my wedding ring when things started going bad. It would have been cutting into me had it still been on. Within three days of it first appearing I was referred to Accident & Emergency by my GP.

Once past A&E reception and the assessment nurse I was taken to a cubicle and met a junior doctor. She decided to do some blood tests and get a couple of X-rays before letting the senior doctor decide what to do. The senior doctor decided it was an infection but was unsure whether to operate on me there in A&E or in theatre. He asked me which I'd prefer; very nice to be consulted I suppose but how was I to know? I said I had no idea but when he mentioned that theatre would involve an overnight stay in hospital I opted for there and then.

They seemed to have a bit of trouble finding all the necessary equipment but eventually I was given a local anaesthetic by injection into my palm, following which it felt like my finger was being blown up like a balloon. Then the doctor very skilfully removed my fingernail and cleaned it up. Unusually, he said, the infection seemed to come from the nail rather than the pulp. Once cleaned and trimmed he replaced it, assuring me that a new nail would grow underneath. I was bandaged up and had to spend an hour with my hand in the air before they would let me go, during which I felt like a little boy hoping to ask permission to use the designated facilities.

Of course, a bandaged finger evoked a lot of concern from friends and family but it was not particularly painful. Several follow-up appointments took place in the fracture clinic over the next few days. It was an interesting waiting area, full of people in plaster or bandaged up here, there and everywhere. During the long waits to be seen, it helped pass the time wondering how the injuries had occurred. Young man with plastered legs – a motorbike accident maybe? Schoolchild with bandaged arm and other scars – fell off a wall perhaps? Older man with missing finger – lost control of the chainsaw while trimming a tree in the garden?

When it was my turn to be seen, the nurses asked how my injury had occurred. Their curiosity seemed very natural and part of the routine in this department of the hospital. There are other departments where such inquisitiveness is probably discouraged. Casually asking, "How did you get that?" is hardly appropriate in the sexually transmitted diseases clinic, for example. It also made me realise it was a question that never arose from the nurses in the cancer ward. In fact, not even the doctors expressed any interest in, or opinion on, how my tumour might have started. When the nurses asked about my finger I felt rather ashamed of my dull reply. There were no chain saws involved and not even a fracture for them to X-ray. "It's just the side effects of chemo," I apologised. They looked a bit disappointed.

It was a couple of weeks later that a finger on my other hand started leaking puss from under the nail too. Fiona bandaged it up so I had a matching pair; the fourth finger on each hand. We returned to the fracture clinic for both nails to be looked at.

The doctor decided to release the pressure that had built up on the original finger and squeeze out the puss. This involved a local anaesthetic injection and the removal of my fingernail again. He did not put it back this time though, saying it may have been preventing the puss escaping. I was given more antibiotics to clear up the infection and hopefully control what was happening on my other hand, which seemed to be going the way the first one went. In fact, all my fingernails were looking pretty bad by this stage and a good squeeze often produced a little smelly, oozing liquid - putrefied nail bed I suppose. My thumbnails were quite loose too and I was worried they would come off if caught on something.

Thankfully, as the chemo had ended at the beginning of February, no further deterioration occurred. As I write it is eight months later. All my nails have recovered and look fine, except the one that had the nail removed. It still has a large dull-yellow patch but given a few more months should be good as new. I wish I could say the same for my toenails!

It was March before my toes started going really bad. They had suffered similar effects to my fingernails during chemo but not as heavily. Unlike my fingernails they seemed to get worse once the chemo finished rather than better. So I was back at the doctor's in March. Swabs were taken, more antibiotics prescribed and I waited for the results. Virtually all previous swabs had shown no specific growth and I expected nothing from these either. It was a surprise when I was told they had identified something. The doctor gave me its name but I only half registered it as some initials.

It was only later in the day when I was visiting a friend recovering from a hernia operation that it dawned on me she had said MRSA, the hospital 'super bug' so often reported in the papers. Hoping I had not passed it on to my friend, whose hernia wound was still very fresh, I returned home to check if I should be in isolation. Apparently not. In fact, MRSA is fairly common in the outside world. It is not a problem for most of us but in hospitals it can get into wound infections and be very dangerous.

So, more antibiotics and more swabs, but eventually I was given the all clear on the MRSA front. Toenails grow so much more slowly than fingernails and the gnarled remains of my left big toenail, which would not look out of place on an ogre, never recovered. Will I ever be able to wear sandals again without my kids pulling faces in disgust?

FROM:	**FIONA MAGGS**
DATE:	**21 MARCH 2006**
TO:	**OUR NETWORK OF FRIENDS AND FAMILY**
SUBJECT:	**MARCH UPDATE ON CHRIS**

Thought it was about time to update you all on Chris and let you know what we are doing. It's his birthday today and what a year it has been!

Since his chemotherapy ended he has been improving gradually. For the first two or three weeks he felt really rough and was sleeping every day. After that he started to improve and his energy and concentration levels are increasing each day. He still needs to sleep but now it is usually every three days. I am encouraging a programme of rehabilitation which involves household duties and sorting through cupboards and drawers!

Chris went for another scan on 3rd March to check the progress of the tumour. We went back to clinic for the results last week and the Consultant was very pleased. The tumour has continued to shrink and compared to the November scan is now relatively small. He has now arranged for the radiotherapy to go ahead. I think there has been a rather longer gap than we were initially expecting as they were not sure whether other treatment would be needed first before the radiotherapy. So now we are waiting again for three appointments. One for an echocardiogram and another for lung function tests. Both of these are needed before the radiotherapy as the heart and lungs may be affected (one of the chemo drugs can also affect the heart). The third appointment is for the simulator, the machine that will scan and plot the radiotherapy target area and Chris will be tattooed to mark the spot.

Life is still strange and the timescale keeps moving. We had thought that the treatment would be over by the end of March but it may now not be finished until May. Chris is unsure as to when he will be able to go back to work although is feeling much more able now and has booked himself onto a course at the beginning of June to refresh his pensions knowledge. Although we feel unable to plan anything at the moment we are confident that progress is being made and Chris is continuing to improve. God has been very good to us and we have experienced his love and support throughout a very difficult year. We also thank all our many friends for their love and prayers which have had a big influence on us and the family. Lots of people ask how the children are doing and the answer is they just get on with it. They seem to have adjusted very well and cope with their dad's illness. They have also shown great faith and trust that God will be with them and that he will enable their dad to get better. I'm sure your prayers have helped them as well. Thank you for your interest in our family and again for your prayers.

Love from Fiona

THE GOOD, THE BAD AND THE UGLY

Over the course of my treatment I have had the pleasure of attending five different hospitals, all within the NHS. I mentioned much earlier in my account how uncomfortable I felt about hospitals previously. Now I consider myself a veteran patient, though for obvious reasons I still have no wish to spend a lot of time in them.

It has surprised me how very different the hospitals are. Each has its own character and feel. Each has good points, bad points and downright ugly points. Here are my thoughts on how varied my experiences of them were – on a "no names" basis.

Hospital A

This was a relatively small hospital with a modern low-level building in a semi-rural setting. Car parking was not too bad, though the barriers seemed to break down frequently and were replaced by little men sorting out tickets.

Once past the one or two smokers loitering outside the entrance, there was a clean and welcoming reception and an extremely well presented café area run by voluntary staff. We only took tea there a couple of times, and I must say the quality of the scones did not live up to my expectations, but even so it was good to find a busy social area right there in the heart of things.

I experienced several parts of the hospital; Respiratory Clinic, X-ray Department, Oncology Suite, Accident & Emergency, Fracture Clinic, blood tests, the Warfarin Clinic, plus a couple of small surgical procedures and the discharge lounge. The staff were all friendly and helpful and though there were occasionally some very long waits, there were also occasions when we were surprised by the speed and efficiency with which we were dealt with.

Unfortunately, the hospital is regularly under threat of losing some of its services. The Trust for the county has to manage its budgets and sometimes proposes consolidating certain services at its main city-centre hospital. Inevitably there is a local outcry, and rightly so. This was happening during my treatment, though not in the oncology area. It was the sort of campaign I would have taken little interest in previously but being more familiar with the hospital I followed progress through the local papers. However, I found myself too open minded to be an activist. I think I signed a petition at one stage but the idea of attending a vigil or taking part in a march would be pinning my colours to one particular mast when in fact I can see arguments on both sides. Of course we want to have local services but we cannot have everything we want unless we are willing to pay more in tax to fund the NHS and I doubt the campaign leaders would be marching with that agenda.

Not that I could stand with the members of the Trust Board either. They have difficult decisions to make but seemed unwilling to engage in genuinely open debate, manipulating words instead to give the impression of consultation when in fact decisions had already been made. Add to that the laughably transparent politicians, out to gain public approval and score points against their opponents, and I ended up shaking my head in bemusement and doing nothing. I may justify my inaction rationally but I fear it amounts to the same as someone who takes no interest at all.

Good: Pleasant atmosphere and attractive setting. Quick service at the pharmacy too.

Bad: The queue for blood tests. You have to sit in a corridor and shuffle along one seat every time someone goes in. And when the queue gets too long it gets mixed up with the antenatal clinic (which could be very awkward).

Ugly: Bickering over the future of certain services affecting so many people's jobs and health.

Hospital B

To be fair, I only had one visit to this hospital. That was a consultation with one of the surgeon's registrars. Like Hospital A it was modern, looking more like a low budget hotel than a hospital from the outside. It had a less welcoming reception area, with patients invited to queue at the correct desk to be processed by staff protected by plastic screens like those in banks. We were then directed to another seating area where we waited in the hope that the right people knew we were there. Efficient, but not exactly friendly.

Good: Modern, efficient and convenient.

Bad: Lacking the personal touch.

Ugly: Those protective screens!

Hospital C

This was an old building, situated in an urban sprawl, which made it more difficult to get to and almost impossible to park at.

Once all the spaces were filled up people either improvised or spent their day circling the car park in despair. There was some rough parkland on the dual carriageway as you approached the hospital that looked like the sort of place people get mugged. If they do, at least it's not far to go for medical help. Our visits here were related to my two operations but this involved a number of day trips as well as two stays in a ward.

Being an old-style building the atmosphere was very different to A and B. The entrances were not grand or even obvious, recognisable more because of the gangs of smokers than anything else. Corridors were grubby and utilitarian, stretching like a rabbit warren into the bowels of the decrepit building. Signage was patchy and sometimes when we got to where we had been told to go we found the clinic had moved elsewhere.

The hospital featured in a programme on TV about hygiene. An undercover journalist had got a job as a contract cleaner and revealed a lackadaisical attitude among staff compounded by unrealistic expectations from the management. It was easy to see how this culture had developed when the building itself was tired and past its best. The good news was that a replacement building was under construction.

> **Good:** The medical staff, who managed to keep cheerful and friendly despite working in unpleasant surroundings.
>
> **Bad:** Lack of car parking space – especially when they charged such high rates too.

Ugly: The building and the entrance area. The whole place looked like a run-down industrial estate.

Hospital D

Another urban hospital. Like Hospital C it was an ancient building with bits and pieces added over the years making it look untidy and disjointed. We only made two visits here, both for CT scans. The department was housed in one of the add-on buildings, thrust into a space at a strange angle and with the entrance hidden around the back out of sight.

The waiting room was crowded and too small for the purpose. We sat facing another row of chairs that were so close we touched knees with the people opposite, while pretending they weren't there in the traditional British way. Thankfully new facilities were being built over at Hospital E to replace this one.

Good: Despite the crowded waiting room we were called in quite quickly and dealt with efficiently.

Bad: Four attempts before they got the cannula needle into my arm and then it fell out while I was being scanned. I had to call them back in to point out I was bleeding to death!

Ugly: The cramped waiting room and adjoining toilets (don't ask).

Hospital E

I visited several buildings at this hospital, all quite different. There was a massive high-rise old fashioned hospital building where I went for X-rays, CT scans, a bone marrow biopsy and some other tests. The CT scan area was right down in the basement and it felt like you were descending into some sort of labyrinth. I would not have been surprised if we had bumped into the odd minotaur, especially when passing the hazard signs for the 'nuclear radiation area'.

Most of my cancer treatment, including the chemo and two stays in the ward due to bowel paralysis, took place in a modern purpose-built oncology building. It was light and airy, with a friendly and relaxed atmosphere, small enough to be cosy while still looking highly professional; the closest I've seen as to what a hospital should be like. They've knocked it down now.

Everything has moved across to a new building on the same site. We were in part of this third building for my radiotherapy. It was clean but bare and clinical. To be fair, the building work was still going on and this may have been a temporary state of affairs.

Our final visit took us to the main entrance of the new hospital, where we were greeted with the face of hospitals to come. Our initial impression was that it was like entering a shopping complex. We came through a large foyer, dominated by glass and steel. In front of us was a modern retail outlet and crowds of people milling about. A sign directed us to the out-patient area but it could just as well have been telling us where Marks & Spencer was located.

Entering the out-patients area we were greeted by a massive open space with jauntily-angled glass roof and vibrant coloured chairs. Around the edges were various reception desks and a well-known coffee vendor's counter. It felt a bit like an airport lounge.

I was not sure what to think of it. The obvious intention was to put people at ease with surroundings familiar to other public spaces. I worried that, perhaps, they had tried too hard to make it not look like a medical facility. It was disorientating to arrive at a hospital and be treated like a consumer, enticed by shops and fashionable refreshments. I had come for serious medical treatment, not to relax and hang out in a pleasant atmosphere. And what will it feel like when the vibrant soft-cushioned seats are torn and coffee stained, the glass roof is streaked with slime and half the soft lighting is broken? Maybe it will feel more like a hospital then and I'll be happy.

> **Good:** The atmosphere in the old purpose-built oncology building. I just hope they have been able to reproduce it in their new location.
>
> **Bad:** Lack of car parking spaces once again. Made up for (in part) by an ever-cheerful attendant who always had a smile.
>
> **Ugly:** Being wheeled from the oncology ward to the old main hospital building through the sub-basement – cold, dark and bare, with what appeared to be occasional blood stains on the floor.

FROM:	**FIONA MAGGS**
DATE:	**27 APRIL 2006**
TO:	**OUR NETWORK OF FRIENDS AND FAMILY**
SUBJECT:	**ANOTHER DATE FOR CHRIS**

Thought I would let you all know that Chris will be starting his radiotherapy on Tuesday (2nd May). It has taken much longer than we had expected. It has however given him more time to recover and build up his strength. The spring cleaning is continuing and I have even got him out in the garden a couple of times now. We are trying to do some walking as well and he even had a game of tennis with Luke the other day which he won! Not sure if Luke was just being kind as Chris says that he is not able to run for all the balls!

Chris now has four weeks of daily radiotherapy which should finish on Tuesday 30th May (because of bank holidays) and then he has finished all his treatment. Because of all the delays, the course which he has booked onto starts on Sunday 4th June, only a few days after the end of treatment. He will only need to sit and listen and will not do any of the 'extras' like the trips out or the evening dance so as long as he is well enough he will try to go. Then he will be seeing a rehabilitation person from the insurance company to plan a 'back to work' schedule.

We are also building up to exams with the boys. Tim sits his A levels and Luke is doing a couple of GCSE's a year early plus some of his science modules. Then it will be the summer again. We have made no plans, especially after having to cancel our plans last year. We feel very cautious and just keep waiting to see how Chris is and what happens next.

Thank you once again for praying and for your interest.
Fiona
P.S. The last MRSA swabs came back negative.

THE INCREDIBLE HULK

Like chemotherapy, radiotherapy is a bit of a mystery to most of us. What exactly is involved? One of my children asked if they played the radio at me very loud.

My own expectations were coloured by the 'Incredible Hulk' story. Mild mannered Bruce Banner gets an overdose of radiation and turns into a giant muscle-bound green angry monster, ripping apart his shirt and shoes in the process but rather conveniently still fitting snugly into his trousers. And the machine that applied the Hulk's initial radiation dose was everything you would expect from science-fiction, including the green beams shooting like lasers into his contorting body as his face portrayed unbearable depths of agony. The reality had only one similarity. I did take my shirt off.

The truth may be less interesting than science-fiction but there is some amazing science involved. The idea that waves of energy can be directed into your body as a form of treatment is quite bizarre. Everything else I had experienced seemed to involve sticking needles into me or taking tablets in order to release drugs into my body. Radiation seems far more humane, with no immediate sensation and no drugs causing havoc elsewhere. On 'Star Trek' the doctor had a little handheld contraption that he hovered over an injured body to both diagnose the problem and treat it painlessly. In my opinion, this is the way all medical treatment should be carried out and radiotherapy is the closest thing to it we have so far.

Having said that, radiotherapy is no miracle cure. Its 'treatment' is the wanton destruction of everything in its path. Like chemo, its purpose is to kill cells and the skill of the doctors and radiographers is to make sure it kills the bad cells without doing too much damage to the good ones. The consultant explained that they would only give radiation treatment to a particular area once in a lifetime because of the damage caused to other tissues. In my case it was my throat, lungs, heart and spine that were in the firing line.

The first stage of the treatment simply involved being measured up. Lasers criss-crossed the room and mapped out my face while I lay still. Distances were then calculated and marks made on my body. When they were happy with everything, I had three small dots tattooed across my chest so that they could line me up in exactly the same position every time. I think I'm the first member of my family to have tattoos, though I rarely get the chance to show them off.

The actual treatment took place on a daily basis for just over four weeks, with weekends off for good behaviour. The routine became very familiar. The journey from home usually took about 40 minutes by car. The car park attendant usually moved his traffic cone with a smile to let us into a special parking area. The waiting room was usually fairly busy. I would usually start reading an article in Readers Digest and be called in before I'd finished it. They always asked for confirmation of my date of birth and address at the desk before we went through to the treatment room itself.

The treatment room had no doors but was accessed by a corridor with two angled turns in it. A friend who teaches physics told me this was to prevent radiation escaping. It was a large room, brightly lit and with white walls, floor and ceiling. I had to take my top off and lie on a hard surface with the machine hovering above me. From my position the machine looked like it had a circular 'eye', about 50 cms across with a glass surface. Through the glass I could see some of its internal workings; metal surfaces and coils. In the centre was a hole through which I assume the radiation came. Bits of lead inside the machine could be manoeuvred to control the area receiving treatment.

The radiographers worked in packs. There always seemed to be at least three of them, though the individuals would vary day to day. They were mainly women and each had their own way of doing things. Some were more friendly than others. On the first day Fiona was able to come into the treatment room to see what was happening and even took a picture for her album. Other days she would come through and sit just outside the treatment room. Then one day, one of the radiographers rather haughtily announced that only patients were allowed to come through from the main waiting area. We kept an eye out for her after that and Fiona only sneaked in if she wasn't there.

Positioning was everything. Sometimes I would be pulled and pushed around to get the laser beams perfectly lined up, other times I happened to lie in the right place first time. Then, when they had set the machine to the right dosage they would all leave the room, assuring me they would be back soon. An intermittent beep would sound for about fifteen seconds; a warning that radiation was about to commence. The radiographers, having retreated to their desk outside the treatment room, had to press a button within this period to say they were all safely out of range. Fiona told me they observed me on monitors to make sure I had not moved.

After a short pause the radiation began. Or at least, a continuous beep began, which I took to be the indication that treatment was now in progress. It lasted less than twenty seconds! The radiographers returned and rotated the machine so that it was underneath me and we went through the routine again. Another short blast. Back they came and I was free to get dressed and go. All that for less than forty seconds of treatment!

During the first few days I felt no ill-effects but after that my level of tiredness, still there from the chemo, grew significantly. After a couple of weeks I went back to sleeping every afternoon. My throat started to feel sore and I was worried it would become difficult to eat. We saw the dietician who, thanks to all her professional training, was able to advise me to eat soft things.

The only other effect was more sensitive skin around my chest and back. It developed a sort of sunburn. Fiona had seen a picture of someone on the internet with a large bright red area following radiotherapy but mine was nothing like as bad. I guess my dose was fairly light given that I'd already had chemo. Oh, and I started turning green when I got angry.

FROM:	**FIONA MAGGS**
DATE:	**14 MAY 2006**
TO:	**OUR NETWORK OF FRIENDS AND FAMILY**
SUBJECT:	**YOU ARE INVITED…**

As we are well into our second year of Chris's illness and hopefully nearing the end of his treatment we would like to recognise the part that has been played by our friends and family and also give thanks to God for his sustaining power throughout it all.

We would like to invite you to a service on Sunday 25th June at Dickens Heath Village Church where we are planning to use some of the time to give thanks. I know that some of you live a distance away but we wanted everyone who has been receiving emails from us to know about the service even if you cannot come.

Dickens Heath Village Church starts at 10.00am for coffee/tea and the service starts at 10.30am. We meet at Dickens Heath School. You can get directions to the church by looking at 'Find a Church' on the internet or I can email you a copy of a map if you need one.

If you are planning to come please do let me know so that we have an idea of numbers for the day. If you cannot make it we still want to pass on our thanks for all the prayers and support that you have given. It really has made a difference.

With love and thanks
Chris and Fiona

MY PIECE OF THE PUZZLE

We wanted to find a way to say thank you to friends and family and also to mark off the end of this particular journey. A church service suited perfectly since it allowed us to do so in a context that put God right in the centre of it all, which is exactly how I wanted it expressed. We wanted to recognise our dependence on relationships with God and those around us simultaneously.

When we were thinking through possible dates I had probably not even started radiotherapy but at least we knew when it would happen and that the treatment would all be over by the date planned. So the invites went out and then I had to start thinking about what I actually wanted the service to include and what I would say. I could not recall ever having been to such an occasion. The closest experience would probably be a thanksgiving service for the life of someone who had died! And I suppose that's what it would have been if the cancer had run its course.

Instead we were giving God thanks for... well, what exactly? Not for successful treatment necessarily. Though all the signs were good it was too early to give the 'all clear'. The cancer could still be active in my chest or even elsewhere, though I did not think it was. But what I wanted to do was to say thank you to God for being our firm foundation throughout one of life's toughest storms. There may be others ahead, even greater ones maybe. Cancer could return or life may throw any number of other horrors at us, but none of that would detract from the thanks I wanted to express for what I believed God had done on this particular journey.

In my mind I felt that, even if I knew the treatment had not worked and the tumour was still growing, I would still have the same desire to give thanks because God had been with me. I would hope to have such faith, though I dare not claim it categorically without the proof.

On the morning of the service it was really uplifting to see so many faces. As well as our church family, all our brothers and sisters and parents were there, along with some friends who had travelled quite a distance. But most surprising was the number who joined us from our old church, which we left in September 2002 in order to be involved in starting a new church in Dickens Heath. It was a feeling I struggle to express. Humbling in a way but at the same time very uplifting. Just to hug and greet so many people who had come there for us was a pleasure in itself, before the service even began.

Probably the biggest thing I've learned on my journey through ill-health is a better appreciation of God at work through the church. Via these people, flesh and blood, God dispenses his love in hugs, in care and concern, in practical help and in genuine friendship. I believe God is working in other ways as well but recognising God in the smiles of his people has been profoundly real. And this morning service allowed me to look out over a sea of such faces and see God.

So what did I say? I tried to express something of how I felt God had been suffering within and alongside me—the 'Jesus has Chemo' idea I've explained earlier. I tried to tell people how, on this journey, God's presence was not something I was constantly aware of but at crucial points he led me through. I tried to put into words what it felt like to hit rock bottom and find the rock I'd hit was God himself. Here was the crux of the matter. Did my faith live up to its own claims? When the chips were down, was there any depth to this Christianity I had been brought up with and had chosen to live my life by? In a sense, through this experience, I had unwittingly put God to the test. The result was that my belief in God not only remained strong but also had more substance. 'Hitting the rock' was not a pleasant experience but it proved to me that the rock was real.

And after that, buoyed up by so many supportive faces, I spoke about the big question of why God allows suffering at all. It is a question I have pondered over many times. I know people are all different; some are activists, some more reflective, some focus on practical things while others prefer theory. I list dangerously towards the reflective side and pondering the imponderable is, for me, the mental equivalent to taking a hot foamy bath. I do not pretend to have all the answers but I enjoy exploring the questions.

At the beginning of the service, as people were arriving, everyone was given a piece of a jigsaw. As we started to approach the big question of suffering I asked each person to take a look at their piece and tell me what they thought the full picture was. There is always a moment when, standing at the front of church, you dread such an illustration falling flat on its face. If someone had shouted out that it was obviously a Spanish port on a clear sunny day, with sailing boats in the harbour and villas on the hillside, I would have had to move on quickly. But instead, someone thought there might be some buildings, someone else said it was the sea, another person suggested a garden, someone else saw only clouds.

I invited them to compare their piece with the people around them, maybe even try to join them together. It didn't help them much. After a while I explained that it was a 1000 piece puzzle, and with only just over 100 people present we were missing too many pieces even if we all worked together. To each individual the big picture was unclear. But yet we could tell there was some design. Even if the image on our own piece was no more than a blur we could see that it had been formed purposefully and that it would fit with other pieces.

It was, of course, a simplistic illustration of our lives. Any of us sees only our own piece in detail and glimpses of other pieces around us. We cannot hope to see or understand the full picture from where we are. But I believe God, who made the puzzle, knew the picture from the beginning.

This still does not answer the question of suffering though. It merely sets the question in a wider context and helps us to come to terms with our limited perspective. There is a tendency in parts of our culture to scoff at anything spiritual as if mankind's intellect has broken through the mists of religion and discovered everything to be false except our own thinking. Such arrogance is not new I suppose. Every age thinks it is living in 'modern times' and standing at the pinnacle of human achievement, only to be demoted to history by the relentless passing of the years. True enlightenment is the humble acceptance of how little we know. As a Christian I embrace my own smallness in the context of an infinite God and part of that includes recognising that I do not have all the answers. There has to be an element of trust.

Even so, God has given us some intellect and a hunger to wrestle with the great unfathomable questions; to engage with his mysteries. We develop a level of understanding as we go through experiences and learn from others people. He gives us insights too. Unfortunately, many make the mistake of thinking they have grasped it all. It is an easy mistake to make, especially when young. As we get older we start to see a pattern emerge; a pattern in which old understandings of things repeatedly give way to new ones, like a snake shedding its skin we leave the old perception behind and wonder that we could ever have inhabited something so dry and lifeless.

As a Christian, a follower of Jesus, I believe my journey should follow the same dynamic principle, frequently catching new glimpses of God, or rediscovering some aspect of my relationship with him in a fresh way. To my mind, created nature partially expresses the infinite diversity of God's nature, so as I marvel at some exotic creature's habits described in a TV wildlife programme or come over the brow of a hill to take in a new landscape, I experience something of that vastness beyond myself. It is the same if I read something in the Bible that hits me with new vigour or if I sense the glory of God in the words of a song. All these things open my heart and mind, if I let them, to God's revelation.

I tried to cover all this ground in the service by way of a caveat to what I was about to give as an answer to the question of suffering. I do not pretend it is the full answer or that I may not develop in my own understanding in the future. I am conscious too that any answer will always sound glib. I said at the service itself that I only dared to stand at the front and give my views on suffering because of my own recent experiences.

Internal abstract thoughts are of little consequence to anyone but ourselves. They become a little more meaningful when they have borne some weight and proven themselves. It was my cancer that gave me the confidence to set out my thoughts to other people but even then I was aware that my suffering has been small compared to many. Do I have the right to pontificate? It is a problem that cannot be easily resolved. Each of us can only speak from the perspective of the life we have.

So I went on to explain my understanding of suffering as an inevitable consequence of freewill. When God created us he gave up his ultimate control over all things. He gifted us with the power to determine the future. Instead of God managing and directing all things, he handed over some responsibility to us.

It was an awesome thing to do, especially when he knew full well that we would not always do what was right. He created an environment for us to live in that ran by strict physical rules and then hid himself away so that we could only find him if we chose to search him out. The world we live in now is, in a sense, an artificial environment. We naturally assume that the physical world we have always known is permanent and all there is. But God has given us glimpses of a spiritual dimension that is far more real than anything we have ever known. He has promised to bring this spiritual dimension fully into our world at some stage but in the meantime, in order to allow us to exercise freewill without being overwhelmed by the presence of God, we are left with the world as we know it. Suffering in this world comes about because of God's decision to give us that freewill and allow us to choose our own path.

This still leaves the big question, why would God do this? If he knew it would involve suffering, why set it up this way? I believe that, in his wisdom, he decided this would lead to the best eternal relationship between man and God. I recognise my answer is not entirely satisfactory from a human perspective because we naturally think of human suffering in this world as the biggest priority. How could God justify it for the sake of something else, we think. It comes back to perspective and trust again. A toddler does not fully understand why her mother scolds her for running into the road. She wails in lament at the sense of rejection the scolding brings. In her worldview the tragedy of a broken relationship with her mother is paramount. She has no understanding of why her mother puts the closeness of their relationship secondary to rules about the road.

Or to put it another way, Jesus told a story about a wealthy farmer with two sons. The younger one asked his father for his share of the inheritance. The father could have said no. He could have insisted his son remain dependent on him, protected within the confines of his family home. Instead, the father let him have the money, knowing full well that he would not spend it wisely. The son left home soon after and chose to live in a different country where he squandered all his wealth.

Just as he ran out of money, the country he was in came under the grip of a famine. Without friends or food, the son started to get hungry. He managed to find a low-paid unpleasant job but he was barely getting by. He suffered. He suffered because his father had given him the freedom to make his own choices. He suffered because of those choices and the choices of the people around him. He suffered because of an indiscriminate natural disaster. All the elements of human suffering are there.

It would be a sad story if that were the end of the matter. It would be sadder still if he had resolved in his mind that ultimately it was all his father's fault for letting him have the money and leave. He could have become angry and bitter and resolved never to see his father again. He could have chosen to mentally cut himself off and deny his father even existed. He did none of those things. Jesus says he came to his senses. He realised that even the workers at his father's house were better off than he was. He decided to go home and apologise. He would say, "I am no longer worthy to be called your son. Please treat me as one of your hired staff."

It must have been a long and hard journey back but when he was still a distance away his father saw him and ran to meet him. He threw his arms around his son who started the speech he had been rehearsing but his father would not even let him finish it. The father welcomed him back as his long-lost son, throwing a party in his honour and rejoicing at the renewed relationship.

Having told this story I pointed out that it was not only the son who had been suffering. His father had suffered too. The son's actions had broken his heart and he yearned for his return. When he made the decision to give his son freedom of choice he knew it would mean suffering for them both. But now he had returned, the whole experience was worthwhile. Now the relationship was so much better. The father did not love his son more – he had always loved his son fully. But the son had experienced the depth of his father's love. The son could now reciprocate that love and wanted to live in permanent relationship with his father.

Some will still say it is not right. If God just wants a reciprocal relationship with man why not simply set it up to be so in the first place? God could have made a perfect world from the beginning with no suffering. Surely that would have been better.

There was an older brother in the story Jesus told. He stayed on the farm and remained in relationship with his father throughout. His father loved him and he loved his father. He worked for his father and was happy to be dependent on him. It was a good relationship. But his reaction when his brother returned showed up some disappointing truths. He said to his father, "Look! All these years I've been working for you and never disobeyed your orders. Yet you never gave me even a young goat so I could celebrate with my friends. Yet when this son of yours who has squandered your money with prostitutes comes home, you kill the fattened calf for him!"

I think the father's reply must have been weighed down with sadness. "My son, you are always with me, and everything I have is yours." Somehow his older son had missed out on the depth of the whole relationship he had with his father. Somehow he had not seen the full richness that was before him. It was the younger son, by walking a path of suffering, who discovered it.

FROM:	**FIONA MAGGS**
DATE:	**1 AUGUST 2006**
TO:	**OUR NETWORK OF FRIENDS AND FAMILY**
SUBJECT:	**ANOTHER UPDATE ON CHRIS - AUG 2006**

It is ages since I sent anything round and I have been meaning to bring everyone up to date for a while.

Life has been ticking along in the Maggs household now for some time. Chris finished his radiotherapy at the beginning of June. He ended up with a few extra days being added on at the end. This was to give a final extra blast to his front. He had been having the radiation given from the front and the back. In the middle of the treatment they blocked out his spine with lead to prevent too much damage. He has a brown patch on his back that looks like he has been burned but that is now the only evidence that it ever happened. His front is a mass of scars and burst blood vessels so it is difficult to see anything there!

He found the treatment was not difficult and although he did develop a sore throat after a week or so it never really got too bad. We saw the dietician and were armed with soft food diet sheets and the offer of food supplement drinks but he never managed to be unable to eat!!! Tiredness was the main thing that was a challenge and he went back to his old routine of sleeping every afternoon.

Since then he has been slowly regaining his strength and building up his stamina with activities at home and exercising his brain cells by auditing some books for a Christian organisation. That kept him at his desk for many a happy hour and has given him a work type activity to do. He has found that he has been able to concentrate to do the job and he now feels able to face the world of work again. The insurance company and his employer are just starting the process of planning a return to work programme. They are not pushing him at all and have told him to take plenty of time to recover! I imagine that he will be back working part time maybe by September. We have no idea how long to full time.

We saw the oncologist last week for a check up and he is very pleased with Chris' progress. We are going to transfer back to our local Redditch hospital so there should not be any more trips to Coventry. The Consultant has asked for another scan to be done and this should be in about 6 weeks time. We will be seeing him now every three months for the next couple of years and then 6 monthly until 5 years. There will be examinations and blood tests at every visit but it is really just waiting to see if any symptoms return over time.

Chris has also had an appointment with an ENT (Ear, Nose and Throat) doctor. This is someone that we know from church who arranged for Chris to go to the ward and have a small camera put down his throat. She had noticed that his voice was not normal earlier in the year and offered to have a look. It was discovered that one of his vocal cords (you have two) is paralysed. This means that there is damage to the nerve supplying it which we know runs through the area in which the tumour was. There is still some scar tissue in the area and this nerve is unlikely to recover. This means that he will not be singing in public again!! His speaking voice has recovered to a reasonable level but when he sings or if he tries to shout he produces a strange sound! His breathing is not back to normal yet and we have not really ascertained whether this will get any better or not. At the moment there is a lot of wait and see!

The family are growing up and we are awaiting exam results for Tim and Luke. Tim is hoping to get to Portsmouth University so our family life will undergo a major change (again) at the beginning of October. Luke starts his GCSE year and Hannah goes into her last year at Junior school.

Life is very strange really at the moment. We say that we are getting back to normal but I am not sure really what normal is! With facing such a major life event there is a sense that you need to do something with it and not really go back to the old normal but we are still working through that and there are no life changing decisions that we have made or are even thinking about making at the moment.

I am sure that there are things God has planned for us but maybe it is too early to be changing at the moment. In some ways the last 18 months seem almost a dream. When I read about what happened in the diary that Chris has kept it seems unreal to remember that it all happened to us. But the fact that God has been very close and supported us through the whole episode is very real. Who knows what will happen in the future? We don't, but we trust in a God that does.

With love and thanks yet again for all your prayers and concerns for us over this time especially,
Fiona

ON THE MEND

I have never run a marathon. I did go through a couple of phases of jogging in earlier years but, to be honest, I haven't got the body for it. Even before I was ill I ran out of breath very quickly when running and then spent the rest of the time fighting to pay off the overdraft. My loud panting was embarrassing and I took to crossing the road to avoid approaching women from behind in case my heavy breathing alarmed them. In my school days I remember finishing last in cross country and once suffering the humiliation of patronising applause as I crossed the finish line well behind the rest. So no marathons for me.

Nevertheless, there was a sense that something physical ought to be done to demonstrate that I had beaten cancer, at least for now. Several people would, by way of encouragement, mention great cancer sufferers who had gone on to win the Tour De France or the Grand National. I felt the pressure was on to emulate their achievements. Tennis is my preferred sport so I set my sights on Wimbledon. And I am proud to say that in June 2006 I was there. Okay, so watching Wimbledon isn't quite the same as playing but it's a start and we had a great day out.

I did make a tentative return to the local tennis courts as a player too. I went with my son Luke and daughter Hannah during the day, when nobody was around to watch. Hitting the ball was not too much of a problem if it was near me but when I had to move for it my brain and legs fell out, and I fell over. It was only a graze but being on Warfarin to thin my blood meant I bled a lot, so my return to sporting prowess had to wait another few weeks. Despite this setback, as my physical stamina returned I took great pleasure in being back on the court. Fellow tennis players at the club have been very concerned for me and have eased me back in gently. The great thing about tennis is that however badly I play, there are always one or two shots that go sweetly and those are the ones I seem to remember best.

The road to recovery is a long and slow one. I have consistently underestimated the amount of time it would take for each stage of my treatment and the same miscalculation continued as I recuperated. Returning to work was something I started anticipating soon after radiotherapy was finished at the beginning of June. I was told by my contact at work to take June off and they would be in touch at the beginning of July. When no call came I contacted them mid-July and they said they would start putting the wheels in motion. The wheels seemed to move very slowly through the rest of July and well into August so I called again to ask what was happening. Eventually I persuaded them that I was ready and it was all set up for me to begin a phased return from 6 September.

This may give the impression, quite wrongly, that I was chomping at the bit to get back behind my desk. The thought of returning to work did not fill me with joy. In fact, there was some trepidation about the catching up I would need to do and whether I could still carry the responsibilities associated with my role. But I knew that going back to work was an important part of my recovery; sort of reclaiming my life in a way. The cancer had taken not just my health but my functionality too. I am not just talking about status. My work is the biggest time commitment of my normal life and the means by which I provide for my family. In that sense it defines a large part of who I am.

I remember talking to friends at church and trying to explain the change of identity that is involved in becoming a full-time cancer patient. I became very passive, partly due to my condition but also because patients are expected to spend so much time waiting around and resting while other people take the initiative. The pace of life slows right down. It is the same, on a smaller scale, when you take a relaxing holiday. Often the first few days feel uncomfortable because the sense of urgency in normal life has nothing to apply itself to. Then you gradually unwind and get used to a more leisurely approach. Far too soon the holiday is over and you are back to work, your body chemistry struggling to catch up with the old stress levels. I always used to get a headache on that first day back.

As I write this I am still in the process of a phased return to work. It seems to be going well. I am more tired as I gradually make increasing demands on my mind and body but it is manageable and an inevitable part of the recovery process. I am extremely grateful for the patience and understanding of my colleagues and the people who are overseeing my progress. I feel like I am still in the foothills with the mountain ahead of me but mountains are there to be conquered and I am confident I will get there if my health continues to improve.

Putting all these written pieces together has been an interesting part of the process too. I hesitate to say it has been part of the recovery. It has been necessary to re-read diary entries and relive the experiences in order to put them onto paper, making me dwell on these events when I might otherwise have been focussed elsewhere. I am not sure that is a good thing. I feel now that I want to move on. This episode in my life has certainly shaped me, as all experiences do, but I do not want it to define me. I do not want to be branded 'brave cancer survivor' in every context. In that sense it is refreshing even now to meet people who do not know about recent events and so avoid the need to assure them, usually more than once, that I am doing fine; "No, really, I am".

It is not that I want to forget or not talk about it. I hope that it will give me opportunity to help others and gain insights into situations I would have missed otherwise. I just do not want it at the forefront of my thinking as it has been for such a long time. I look forward to the day when I will have to remind myself, "Oh yes, I had cancer once."

For those of you who have battled your way through our account of events and my self-indulgent meanderings, I hope you have found some things of value in amongst the debris. I have deliberately mixed the routine with the spiritual, the mundane with the amazing, the disappointments and sufferings with the triumphs because that is what our life is made up of. It is a messy concoction I admit but I would not have it any other way.

If I have to draw anything out of it all, it would simply be that, whatever the circumstances, God is good. I am convinced that nothing can separate us from his love and it is often the hardships that make us realise what is truly worthwhile.

PART TWO

JESUS HAS CHEMO AGAIN

JESUS HAS CHEMO AGAIN

If you've journeyed with me and my family through our adventures in 'Part One', you will appreciate why I might refer to those two years as a bit of a roller coaster ride. And, of course, with all good roller coasters, just when you think the ride is over there's always another twist to come. I finished writing about the ups and downs of 'Part One' in October 2006 as I was phasing back into full-time work and normality. But it turned out that the 'normality' we experienced for a few months was simply the build up to the top of the roller coaster and a new set of experiences.

It has taken some time for me to get back to the keyboard again and write about it all. This time everything happened more quickly and the treatment was more intense, as a result of which I did not keep a daily diary like I had before. So I have had to rely on memories more and the benefits of hindsight but, as previously, I have tried to be as honest as I can and spare you none of the gory details. Feel free to laugh as well as wince at the various physical torments. Enjoy our triumphs and take pity on our failings. And I pray that as you read our story it will give some insights into the way we understand our faith in God.

In terms of catching up on events on the practical front, when we pick up the story at the beginning of 2007, our son Tim had settled in at Portsmouth University doing Digital Media (don't ask me!), Luke was 15 and in his final GCSE year and Hannah had just turned 11 and was threatening to be as tall as her Mum fairly soon. I had returned to work and both Fiona and I were re-appointed to our Church's leadership team from 1 January 2007. Things seemed to be getting back to normal.

FROM:	FIONA MAGGS
DATE:	11 JANUARY 2007
TO:	OUR NETWORK OF FRIENDS AND FAMILY
SUBJECT:	ANOTHER MAGGS UPDATE

Some of you may know that back in November when we went for our doctor's appointment there was some concern over an area that had shown on Chris' last CT scan. He was sent for another scan a couple of weeks before Christmas - this time a PET scan. This type of scan involved injecting him with a radioactive sugar which is then able to show up any active cancer cells that may be in his body. Today we have been back to the hospital for the results. Unfortunately the news is not good. There is still an area of the original tumour that has not responded to the chemotherapy and radiotherapy. This means that Chris now has to undergo more intensive treatment. He has to have a number of initial tests before starting some more chemotherapy.

We will be seeing another consultant in Coventry for this new treatment so the actual times and details are all a bit vague at the moment. What we know at the moment is that he will have possibly a couple of medium intensity chemotherapy treatments which this time will last 5 days and will be given in hospital. At the same time they will remove stem cells from his blood and store them. Then the third chemotherapy will be a massive blast which will wipe out his immune system. He will be in hospital for a while and isolated. They will then give him back his stem cells and hopefully his body will start to recover. That is what we understand at the moment although he obviously has to have all the initial tests etc. and things may change. This next treatment regime will take about another 6 months so life in 2007 will not be back to 'normal'.

This would have been Chris' first week back at work full time although we both recognise that he was going to find full time difficult. He is planning now to cut down his time a bit and see how he copes with the initial treatment and maybe work part time if and when he feels well. When he has his major dose of chemotherapy he will need to take at least 3 months or so off work again as he will be unable to do much.

I expect lots of you will be thinking, how do we feel. It's really hard to say. I think we both knew it was a real possibility, in fact I think we went to the hospital expecting the news to be bad. Various things that have happened over the last few weeks, including the speed at which the doctor wanted to see us, have led us to believe this was to be the news. I suppose we are in shock at the moment and have gone straight into 'coping' mode. Chris has gone back to work this afternoon as he is on a course and then later this evening is giving a talk at a consultant actuary meeting. I expect reality will hit when we start making our way back to Walsgrave Hospital.

So, it is back to asking you all to pray for us again. God has been our strength and help throughout the previous two years of this journey and we are confident he will continue to be with us. Please pray for the children (who don't even know yet) that they will be able yet again to cope. Luke has his GCSE's coming up in the summer and this time with Tim being away from home he will not be involved in the same way.

Thank you for caring for our family.
Love Fiona

HERE WE GO AGAIN!

I hardly know where to start in explaining how it all felt when we were told more chemotherapy treatment was needed. Obviously disappointed but, as Fiona said, not entirely surprised.

I certainly wouldn't use the word devastated because having already been through what we had we knew we could face whatever the next stage was. And in some weird way it was comforting to get back into what had become our way of life – hospitals, treatment and hair loss!

My return to the world of work had been more difficult than I thought. Starting in September on just three half-days a week I had gradually built up to full time over four months. Officially my first full-time week commenced on 25 December but as I took all that week and the beginning of the next as holiday my first full five-day week commenced 7 January.

Putting in the hours at the office was not the problem. I did feel tired as the working week built up between September and December but that was to be expected and the phased return seemed to work very well in terms of developing more stamina. But sitting at my office desk and actually working at the right level are two different things. For a start, I knew I was not mentally sharp enough at that stage and it would take time to get back into the cut-and-thrust of the pensions world.

Then there was the difficulty of finding the right things to do. My normal job involves managing a portfolio of clients, juggling their needs and our resources, responding to short and long-term demands and so on. But most of my old clients were being happily managed by my colleagues and those responsibilities I did resume were not enough to keep me fully occupied. There were other things to do, of course, but it still left a sense of not being fully operational – not pulling my weight with the rest of the team.

So I admit to a sense of relief at dropping my work responsibilities and lapsing back into the patient role. Looking back, Fiona recognised I was struggling with tiredness a lot of the time. We put it down to the return to work but the fact that the tumour was still active and using up energy would no doubt have contributed to the mix as well.

On the day we received the news, it happened that I was due to speak at a local meeting of the Association of Consulting Actuaries in the evening. Of course, nobody there knew the position. I had not told anyone at work yet. As one of the speakers that evening I also attended the dinner afterwards. None of my colleagues were at my table so it was easy to carry on superficial conversations without anyone knowing either my recent past or my immediate future. There is always an element of 'putting on a professional face' at these events but I felt particularly conscious of my own façade that evening.

Towards the end of the meal there were some traditional toasts, including the Queen, any new members and, ironically, a toast to the good health of the speakers. It would have been churlish to bring it up at that point. "Funny you should mention my health, as I heard just this afternoon that..."

It was not just me who had to adapt to a sudden change of outlook as a result of our news. Fiona had been gradually returning to normality too, reclaiming our home as her 'patch' while I built up my hours of work. You would have thought that she'd have missed my tired and grumpy demeanour around the place but apparently she likes to be on her own sometimes and to return from a shopping trip to find everything exactly as she left it. Unfortunately, this was not to be the case for a while longer.

It is surprising, perhaps, that our thoughts at this time were largely along practical lines rather than emotional. There were no tears that I can recall, no emotional crisis point. I think it surprised us a little too, but then again we knew we had been carried through a great deal already by the prayers and care of our friends and family. We had already tested the foundations of our faith and knew them to be strong. We had known the storm may not be over yet and so it proved. But we also believed that our God was stronger than the storm.

FROM:	**FIONA MAGGS**
DATE:	**12 JANUARY 2007**
TO:	**OUR NETWORK OF FRIENDS AND FAMILY**
SUBJECT:	**NO WAITING THIS TIME!**

There is more information already to give you, the NHS is working extremely quickly this week! We received a phone call today from the Walsgrave Hospital to say that they had a bed for Chris on Monday morning. (They had a cancellation.) We have to do the usual check to make sure that it is still available at 8.30am but it seems that everything is on to get him in and start chemo next week. We have not yet had any of the information about the treatment or had all the side effects and details explained to us yet. I believe that they are going to do that on Monday morning, we just won't get any time to think about it. However, we already know that we would not decide to put it off or even not to go through with it. So the quicker it starts the less time the cancer has to do its thing. Chris will be having a bone marrow biopsy again, which may happen on Monday but apart from that I have no details about what is going to happen, how long he will be in or what state he will be in when he comes out! We now have two days to get our lives in order and pack the bags.

Thanks for all the messages that came flying back when I sent out the other email yesterday. It does give me a boost to read them and realise that you all care so much about us and what happens.

Love Fiona

P.S. Please feel free to pass our emails onto anyone who you know is interested.

WHAT WENT WRONG?

Everything seemed to be happening very fast. After receiving the news that I still had active cancer on Thursday we were told on Friday that treatment would start on Monday! I had no choice but to tell my boss on the Friday and make some frantic arrangements to pass on various meetings and responsibilities.

I recall sitting down with a couple of people at work that day and breaking the news to them. In myself I felt okay and in control but when I spoke there was a real strain in my voice – a dry throat caused by stresses my conscious mind was blocking out. It was strange to hear the emotion trying to break out physically while I had it under control mentally. And of course the workplace is not usually the place for discussing really heartfelt matters, so the whole environment felt unnatural. It is a shame, I suppose, that we tend to create environments at many workplaces that deter natural human expression.

Talking to friends and family was much easier, especially where we shared a faith in God. Much prayer was offered up for speedy effective treatment and recovery but also for God's support through the process. As far as I recall, nobody asked the question, "What went wrong?" but I suspect it would have passed through many people's minds if not directly in their prayers. After all, hadn't they been praying over all the previous months that God would heal me through the various treatments? And hadn't we given thanks to God back in June for bringing me through? I had even been dubbed 'Miracle Man' by one godly lady whose husband had been taken by cancer that same year.

I'm sure the question must have presented itself to me at times as well, though I dismissed it easily. It had never been part of my expectation that God was committed to heal me as a result of my faith or the prayers of others. Prayers are only ever requests and the decisions are left in his hands. Those who truly trust in him are happy for him to decide the outcome. In fact, it is best expressed by the words I put together to describe how I felt about the thanksgiving service we held in June 2006.

"We were giving God thanks for… well, what exactly? Not for successful treatment necessarily. Though all the signs were good it was too early to give the 'all clear'. The cancer could still be active in my chest or even elsewhere, though I did not think it was. But what I wanted to do was to say thank you to God for being our foundation throughout one of life's toughest storms. There may be others ahead, even greater ones maybe. Cancer could return or life may throw any number of other horrors at us, but none of that would detract from the thanks I wanted to express for what I believed God had done on this particular journey.

In my mind I felt that, even if I knew the treatment had not worked and the tumour was still growing, I would still have the same desire to give thanks because God had been with me. I would hope to have such faith, though I dare not claim it categorically without the proof."

Well, now was the time for some of the proof. Things had not worked out how I and those around me would have wished. Was it time to give up on God? No way! It was time to cling to him more closely. After all, who else could journey with me all the way, even through death itself, and out the other side?

I'm conscious in writing this that it may sound rather pious. I have not suffered as intensely as many people have around the world, either through persecution or poverty or war. I am not pretending to be a great man of faith. Most of the time I do not float five centimetres above the ground and emit a holy glow from the back of my head. My life is largely routine and mundane and there are few opportunities for the bare metal of my faith to be shown. In that sense I am glad to have had the opportunity to face some difficulties in order to declare my trust in God and hopefully be an encouragement to others. In this, as in all things, I want him to be honoured.

FROM:	**FIONA MAGGS**
DATE:	**15 JANUARY 2007**
TO:	**OUR NETWORK OF FRIENDS AND FAMILY**
SUBJECT:	**CHANGE OF PLAN**

Everything changed today! When we rang for a bed at 8.30 there was not one available until later in the day. Then after discussion with the new Consultant and the Lymphoma specialist nurse it was decided that it was unfair on Chris to get him in so quickly before any of the preliminary information had been given about the treatment and all that it entails. So, new arrangements have now been made. He is to go for an echocardiogram on Wednesday morning and then we are going to meet the new Consultant who will talk to us about what she is planning to do. There may be more tests on Thursday and/or Friday and then they will start chemo next Monday.

All of this is keeping us on our toes! Chris was a bit deflated when we got the phone call to give us the change of plan as he had mentally prepared himself for today. However, he did go into work this afternoon and plans to do a couple more half days this week. He can now admit how tired he is feeling now he knows there is a valid reason.

Sorry to all of those of you who were praying for us in the hospital when we were actually sat at home drinking coffee! Your prayers were very effective last night though as we both slept well again despite the nervousness we both felt about today.

Thank you for praying for us
Fiona

IN AND OUT

The Wednesday echocardiogram and subsequent consultation were quite straightforward and arrangements were made for the first week of chemotherapy to start on the 22nd (the following Monday). It was good to be able to run through the basics of what was going to happen and get a better understanding of it all.

We came away with the usual information sheets on the concoction of drugs that would be used. The regime was called ESHAP for those interested. There were four different chemotherapy drugs with long nasty sounding names and all with similar side effects of tiredness, nausea, anaemia, diarrhoea or constipation, fertility loss, reduced resistance to infection, hair loss and loss of appetite. Some had extra nasties like 'gritty eyes'.

It all made for cheerful reading as I packed my bag and sought out various amusements to help the days pass when in hospital.

The delayed admission to hospital allowed us time to make a brief trip to Portsmouth to spend some time with Tim and enjoy a family weekend together. We explored the delights of the old naval dockyard there, visiting Nelson's ship Victory and being shocked, as ever, by history and the realisation of how hard life was for the crew. If nothing else it makes you appreciate how well off we are in our modern age, whatever we are facing. At least we don't have to wash our clothes in our own urine!

Then it was back home and straight into hospital. This time I was actually going in feeling quite well for a change. I would come out feeling a lot worse, with the full effects of the drugs' cumulative effects kicking in over several days and weeks. But on arrival, I was fairly jolly and settled in easily.

Because of the nature of the treatment on the haematology ward, virtually all rooms are single and en suite to keep patients isolated. But the staff were friendly and as they settled me into my room it felt a bit like going on holiday - admittedly a fairly cheap holiday given the sparse nature of the accommodation and facilities, like a Travelodge with nurses.

Actually, that may not be too far from the truth. This was a new hospital building, funded by the Government's private finance initiative. So the building was commercially owned (though not by Travelodge) and rented to the hospital. As a result, nothing could be done to the fabric of the room without the owner's permission and this was frequently cited as the reason why various fixtures and fittings were in the wrong place or not working. Progress, as ever, seems to take us backwards.

Within a few hours of arrival I was hooked up to a drip, which was to remain my constant companion for most of my stay. Some of the drugs had to be dripped in over several hours, including overnight, and I only had enough time for a quick shower occasionally before being plugged back in again. The rest of the time I was sitting in bed or in the high back chair reading, doing puzzles or sleeping, with the latter taking up more and more time as the week progressed.

It was nice to get visitors. Family and friends came and Fiona was there every day as well. I also got a visit from one of the chaplains. My Mum and Dad had manufactured this. They had been at the hospital in the morning, as Mum had an appointment, and they decided to stay for afternoon visiting. To fill the gap between they had been wandering around the hospital when they came across the Multi-faith Prayer Room and went in.

I have never been drawn to these places myself so have little experience of them. The bare quietness does not appeal and there's something rebellious in me that does not want to seek God in a place specifically allocated for that purpose. God is everywhere and I'd rather seek him in the hustle and bustle. Anyway, they fell into conversation with the chaplain and the outcome was that he came to see me later in the day.

I confess I feel a bit intimidated by formal visits from 'men of the cloth', not being sure what I'm supposed to say. As in previous experiences, the conversation remained entirely secular for a long time and I felt uncomfortable that we had not strayed onto spiritual issues at all. Perhaps it is part of their remit not to mention God unless the patient does, to avoid accusations of proselytising, or maybe to avoid infringing health and safety regulations? I felt the pressure to steer things God-ward, so eventually blurted out, "Well, have you got any words of encouragement for me then?" He looked at me rather startled. Then, after a pause he said, "I could pray for you". So he did, and shortly after, left.

The nurses were wonderful, as ever. One stood out though because she was so different in character. She was much more outspoken than the rest and tended to do things her way rather than 'by the book' if she could see an improvement. We got into conversation very easily and, when she noticed my Bible, soon discovered a mutual faith.

She encouraged me with her enthusiasm for God and her willingness to talk about him openly. However, I was upset to find out later in the week that she had been reprimanded for doing so. Well, to be fair, the reprimand was more to do with her forgetting to take my blood pressure while we were talking but the fact that we had got involved in a conversation about faith seemed to be a mark against her and she was told to concentrate more on the job and less on talking. Yet that conversation, more than any with the doctors, nurses or even the chaplain, had lifted my spirits.

There was a placard on the wall opposite my bed that spelled out the objectives of the ward in very grand terms. At the top it referred to the physical, mental and spiritual well-being of the patients as its main priority. I was disappointed to discover that the spiritual aspect of care seemed to have no real substance.

With drugs being dripped into me around the clock there was a constant danger of my body swelling due to the extra fluids. So I was asked to monitor liquid intake and outflow. Every drink had to be recorded on a 24 hour chart and every trip to the toilet involved a measuring jug. I found it most instructive to discover the exact volume of a bladder full. Average levels were around 350 – 450 ml but on occasions I could manage 650-700 ml and was in danger of overflowing the measuring implement. I noticed that my kidneys seemed most industrious during the night and output in the early hours always exceeded the daytime. Regularly dragging myself out of bed in the dark, attached to a drip and collecting all my efforts in a small jug made night times quite disturbed but there was plenty of time for sleep during the day.

The body swelling started within a couple of days. I had to take my wedding ring off while I still could and my legs and ankles blew up very effectively. My bloated state and weight gain were noted by the doctors on the Wednesday and I was prescribed some diuretics. The first lot were pretty ineffective and I was given a stronger dose that evening. As a result I was up ten times that night and produced 4.6 litres of urine – enough for a very effective washday on HMS Victory!

Nausea came and went at various times, though I was rarely actually sick. The anti-sickness tablets and drips did a good job. On Thursday I started some eye drops. They had to be applied every two hours, 24 hours a day for the next six days – another opportunity to disturb my sleep. I reset my watch alarm every time I did them, to wake me up for the next lot.

Inevitably, knowing my bowels, I started suffering constipation too. There was space on my 24 hour recording form for bowel movements as well, though I was pleased to hear I did not have to weigh the output.

Saturday morning brought some relief as the chemotherapy regime finished and I came off the drip. No relief on the bowels front though, and a battery of tablets and laxative solutions were now in play. I half expected to be kept in until I performed but the doctor was happy to let me go.

It was strange to get back into the open air after spending five days cooped up in a single room. Fiona had taken me for a couple of walks down the corridor but those had been my only excursions. Moving about in the real world made me realise how frail I had become even over those few days but it was great to get back home. I had not been eating for the last day or so, what with nausea and constipation problems, so when I did eventually produce the goods later that day I celebrated with my favourite biscuit – a lemon puff.

FROM:	**FIONA MAGGS**
DATE:	**27 JANUARY 2007**
TO:	**OUR NETWORK OF FRIENDS AND FAMILY**
SUBJECT:	**CHRIS IS HOME**

The first part of the treatment is over and Chris has come home today. He is feeling rather nauseous (just a small amount of sickness) and is on a wonderful concoction of medications, creams, mouth washes and eye drops. The eye drops have to be done every two hours (day and night) for the next 5 days so there is not going to be any good sleep for some time. The chemo is also taking its toll and he is feeling tired and generally unwell. He will be at home with no planned hospital visits until next Sunday when he has to go back for blood tests and then on the Monday to have his stem cells collected.

Hannah and I are both unfortunately suffering from colds and coughs so we are trying to keep our distance from Chris and dosing ourselves up with cough mixture. Tim is also unwell in Portsmouth. Luke however is fine. He tells me it is his diet of chips, crisps and chocolate that keeps him so fit and well!!!

That's all for now.
Love Fiona

PSALM THING FOR EVERYONE

In the Bible, the book of Psalms is a collection of songs and poems collected by the Israelites hundreds of years before Jesus was born. While I was in hospital I made a point of reading and thinking about some of them. In fact, I set myself the task of three a day – morning, midday and evening – writing down my thoughts as I went. Looking back at the notes now, it seems my good intentions did not last the full week as I only did ten psalms altogether but I do recall being amazed (as I have been on previous occasions) at how these words, written thousands of years ago by people of a different culture and a significantly different revelation of God, can speak so directly into our current lives. It is a testament to the consistency of human nature throughout the ages and, I think, God's unchanging nature too.

Many of the psalms are written in or about difficult circumstances, so it's not surprising we find common ground in them when we face our own trials. Here are some verses from one of the psalms I found particularly helpful, followed by a few of the things I jotted down at the time.

The note in brackets at the beginning tells us the circumstances in which this psalm was written. The full story is also in the Bible, in the book of 2 Samuel. Nearing the end of his reign as King of Israel, David flees in light of an uprising by his son Absolom. Talk about the world being against you!

Psalm 3 - New International Version

(A psalm of David when he fled from his son Absolom)

v1O Lord, how many are my foes! How many rise up against me!

v2Many are saying of me, "God will not deliver him."

ᵛ³But you are a shield around me, O Lord; you bestow glory on me and lift up my head.

ᵛ⁴To the Lord I cry aloud, and he answers me from his holy hill.

ᵛ⁵I lie down and sleep; I wake again because the Lord sustains me.

ᵛ⁶I will not fear the tens of thousands drawn up against me on every side.

ᵛ⁷Arise, O Lord! Deliver me, O my God! Strike all my enemies on the jaw; break the teeth of the wicked.

ᵛ⁸From the Lord comes deliverance. May your blessing be on your people.

v1: David feels like nobody supports him, although 2 Samuel chapter 15 shows he still had support in some quarters. Perhaps David's words just reflect surprise at the number turned against him. Or maybe, like most of us faced with difficulty, the problems loom so large in his mind he can think of nothing else.

v2: The general opinion seems to be that God is against him too, based on the circumstances they can see.

v3-6: But David knows differently. His words here reveal a close relationship with God. He feels his protection like a shield, one who brings strength and courage, a God who answers prayer and who overcomes David's fears. This is a personal God and I can relate to David's words, especially at this point in my life when, at times, there is nowhere else to turn. God is more than sufficient to sustain us against whatever comes along.

v7: This brings us to David's prayer for God to act. The call is not for total destruction, just a few broken teeth, presumably reflecting David's love for his son – it's more "teach him a lesson Lord" (see 2 Samuel 18 v 5). But should David seek deliverance and conquest or should he just ask for God's will to be done? In the end the uprising was defeated, so perhaps David knew God wanted to return him to power. Or was he simply expressing his own desire? This is an issue I have faced with my own illness – whether to ask for healing or simply that God be glorified in whatever happens. I do not think there is anything wrong with putting our requests before God, in fact there is nothing more natural, but we have to be willing for him to make the decision. 2 Samuel 15 v 25-26 shows David was willing to accept God's will. He says, "If I find favour in the Lord's eyes, he will bring me back… but if he says 'I am not pleased with you', then I am ready; let him do to me whatever seems good to him."

v8: David puts his trust in God for deliverance and ultimately prays for his people to be blessed – maybe allowing for that blessing to come through Absolom if that is God's way. 2 Samuel shows David's mixed emotions at this time very well and I can relate to this.

Another thing I like about the psalms is that they reflect the confusions and contradictions in our human minds as we struggle through problems. Psalm 102 is full of doubts, questions, confidence and trust. I tried to paraphrase it.

Psalm 102 - New Chris Maggs Version

v1-2 Help! I can only turn to you. But will you listen and respond?

v3-11 Things are a bit rough at the moment – and there's a bit of me that blames you.

v12 You don't know what it's like down here.

v13-16 For the sake of your chosen people I know you will act to put things right. You will make your name feared…

v17 …and at the same time save us destitute people.

v18-22 I can see it now – people will look back and marvel at what God did.

v23-28 Of course, I've had it tough from God but I've pleaded with him. He is eternal and I'm confident he will bring his people through everything and establish them forever.

FROM:	**FIONA MAGGS**
DATE:	**7 FEBRUARY 2007**
TO:	**OUR NETWORK OF FRIENDS AND FAMILY**
SUBJECT:	**THE STEM CELLS ARE COLLECTED**

The last few days have been quite traumatic for Chris and we seem to have spent a lot of time in various hospital departments.

On Monday we went to the hospital in Coventry for him to have a line put into his groin for the stem cell harvest but when we got there we were told that his blood test results (taken Sunday) meant that they were not going to do the harvest that day. So, we went home after another blood test. Then later in the day they phoned to say that his bloods were now OK and to go back and they would fit the line and the harvest would take place on Tuesday morning. The fitting of the line is not something that Chris will want to remember! We were told it can be done in 10 minutes or 30 if it is difficult. Chris must have been in the room for one and a half hours. They had a number of attempts in each groin and eventually got one in with much pain, despite the local anaesthetic. He is now very black with bruising.

On Tuesday morning we went to Warwick hospital for the stem cell harvest. This went smoothly and they were looking to collect 1.5 million cells (it would have been back on the machine today if not). We had a call last night to say that they have got 19.2 million so his bone marrow has been very busy. Unfortunately when we got home Chris was feeling quite unwell and went to bed. He had had a bit of a cough during the day. When he woke at around 5pm his temperature had risen and as we have been repeatedly told by the hospital staff we phoned the ward to report it. They wanted him in but as there was no empty bed on the haematology ward we had to go via A&E. This meant an hour wait to be seen and then lots of tests and eventually they put up an antibiotic drip - they think he probably has either a chest infection developing or an infection in the line in his groin. They have kept him in and he will be there for a few days.

We were due to go to clinic this afternoon to sort out the next part of his treatment. We know that the plan is provisionally for him to go back into hospital on the 20th Feb and start his next lot of chemo on the 21st. That will last 6 days and then the stem cell transplant should take place on 27th February. Then we wait for the transplant to graft (start working) and that can take a number of weeks. During that time he will be having a number of blood transfusions to keep him going until his body starts making enough blood cells.

That is life in the Maggs household. Lots of trips down the M6 to Coventry. My motorway driving is getting lots of practice. The children carry on with their school lives. Luke has his mock GCSE's in a couple of weeks so is meant to be revising! He is doing a really good job of being big brother to Hannah. Tim has finished his exams in Portsmouth and is having a week of sleeping before he starts his next semester on Monday.

That is all my ramblings for now. Thanks to everyone who is praying for our family.

With love, Fiona

A BIT BELOW THE BELT

A stem cell harvest used to require a bone marrow transplant because stem cells had to be taken from marrow in the centre of the bone where they are continuously being formed. This was a fairly traumatic procedure as I understand it and may have involved mining various bones to get enough. Now, however, they have found a way of gathering stem cells from the blood and the process is relatively painless.

Or at least, it is relatively painless after you've been fitted with a two-way valve in your groin. Not being so equipped (a little disappointing that God did not make it a natural feature of the human body) I had what I believe was the most painful experience of my whole treatment, as a doctor made repeated attempts to locate a suitable vein and insert the necessary hardware. The procedure, as Fiona pointed out in her email, is not one I like to remember, but for your interest and amusement here are the highlights of the whole groinal experience.

Getting it in: For a start, there's the slight embarrassment of revealing one's privates to complete strangers. But we all pretend there's nothing more normal than removing your undergarments and displaying yourself to a couple of ladies – one a doctor and the other a nurse – while they go about their business just centimetres from your assets. And of course to them, I suppose, it is all very normal. For the record, neither of them gasped in horror or amazement so I take it that 'normal' about sums it up.

The doctor was not the most communicative of people. She must have talked to me before she got started, explaining the procedure, but once she was about the job there was no idle banter or even any indication of what was going on. As the minutes passed away, and the pain began intermittently to break through the effects of the local anaesthetic, I began to hope more and more that we might be nearly done. "How's it going?" I'd ask cheerfully, only to be ignored. I guess she was concentrating on the job (not a bad trait but a little patient acknowledgement would not have gone amiss). Imagine my dismay when, about an hour into the ordeal she said to the nurse, "I think we'll try the other side." So it was like starting all over again.

To be fair, she did talk directly to me once. As she was making incisions into my groin with what felt like a pair of barbecue tongs there were several sharp stabbing pains and I could not help occasional instinctive spasms of movement. "Could you try not to move please!" she ordered rather testily. Obviously she was not having a good day.

The nurse, on the other hand, was a great encouragement. She did what few nurses seem to have time for in the modern system. She cared. She was full of concern, in her face and words, and although I can't be sure I remember this accurately, it certainly felt like she held my hand and suffered with me. I was grateful for her compassion.

While it was in: Because of the trauma of the fitting, I ended up with some tremendous bruises on both sides of my groin. My only regret is that I could not show them to everybody. Fiona even refused to take a picture for her scrapbook of our experiences – perhaps it is for the best.

We went to Warwick Hospital to have the stem cell 'harvest'. One very nice feature of this old style hospital was the welcome committee. At the door was a desk manned by volunteers who offered help to those who needed it. A lady showed us the way to the ward we wanted, which was helpful given that we were a bit late after losing our way in an unfamiliar town centre.

It was a pretty crowded ward. I was in one corner, on the only bed, while the rest of the room was packed with high-back cushioned chairs occupied by people on drips. The group immediately to my right were obviously regulars as they seemed to know each other well. They chatted and laughed their way through the morning as if it were some kind of social club. The staff were friendly too. In fact, I felt so at home in this busy little world that when they asked me to slip off my trousers I was a bit too quick. Apparently I was supposed to wait for them to pull the curtains round!

The man in charge of the process was a medical technician. With his white coat and slightly bumbling manner he reminded me of a mad scientist. The impression was reinforced by the equipment he was using. It looked like something from the sixties and would not have been out of place in 'Thunderbirds' or 'Joe 90'. It had tubes and knobs and switches galore, each of which was carefully set by the man in the white coat.

I remember writing last year on my misconceptions about a blood transfusion, largely based on images recalled from a horror film. Well, this process fitted the misconception quite well. Once I was plumbed into the machine and the switch was turned on, I watched the progress of my blood flowing through the tube into the machine as it whirred and clicked, then out through another tube into a second part of the contraption and finally, once fully processed, back into me. The only thing missing was some organ music and a mad laugh from the technician.

After all the difficulty getting the valve system into my groin it should not be surprising that it would continue to be troublesome. Although it performed the stem cell harvest very well, it was blamed for an infection that took me back into hospital for a couple of days. Getting back into hospital was not so easy as it might have been though.

As Fiona explained, we had to go through Accident & Emergency, which is a pretty soul destroying process. Considering that you have come because you need help, there is little warmth or welcome. We waited an hour in the draught of a persistently opening automatic door and watched the sad procession of hurting and dysfunctional humanity come and go. When we made it to the triage nurse, who makes the initial assessment, it was clear we were just another statistic to be processed – blood pressure, diabetes test, allocation to a cubicle to wait another hour or so for a doctor.

It was all so unnecessary given that we had spoken to the haematology ward before coming and they had left a message with A&E to explain the problem and what to do. We even saw the message scribbled on a piece of paper when we first arrived at the reception desk. But no, we had to be put through the A&E system.

I was seen first by a very junior doctor, then a while later by a less junior doctor and eventually by a doctor who actually knew enough to do something. All in all it took five hours to get through A&E and it was after midnight when I was taken up to the haematology ward. I never thought I'd say this about a hospital ward, but after such a prolonged wait it felt like coming home to be back in familiar surroundings with people I knew.

Getting it out again: While I was in hospital for the infection, and since the offending line was no longer required, it was decided it should be removed. I was assured this was a simple job with no need for any local anaesthetic. So, off with the inhibitions and the pyjama bottoms and once again I lay there trying to relax while the doctor went about his business.

I think the removal went fine, it was just the bleeding that caused some problems. It simply would not stop. And being in a large vein it was a pretty substantial flow. The idea is that after removal of the valve and application of some pressure to the wound the blood will naturally clot to fill the hole. It should take a couple of minutes at most. Five minutes later the doctor was starting to display some signs of concern, not least because his fingers were hurting through the application of continuous pressure.

A nurse was called and she was asked to get another doctor. The other doctor arrived shortly and they took turns to stem the flow, while a couple of nurses looked on anxiously. They decided to bleep the surgeon, not that there was any cause for concern they assured me, just as a precaution. It would probably stop soon. But no, every time they released the pressure the flow of blood returned. Someone decided to put another line into my arm in case I needed extra fluids. "Was it okay," they asked casually, "if they called my next of kin to let them know I might be going into emergency surgery?" The doctor seemed to think that more pressure was the key and pushed down so forcefully it was painful. I was glad when one of the nurses took over and adopted a gentler approach.

About twenty minutes into the exercise the surgeon arrived. By now there were probably three other doctors, half a dozen nurses and possibly a couple of cleaners too. My genitalia have never had such an audience. One of the nurses did try to cover my modesty with a sheet but the doctor insisted he needed to see 'everything' and I was left fully exposed. Although the doctor who started the procedure was clearly distressed by developments, the surgeon was a much more relaxed fellow who strode into the room making humorous quips and calmly suggesting one or two ideas – the most pertinent being to keep the pressure on and let it sort itself out. And so we proceeded for another twenty minutes or so. "It's not every day a pretty blonde nurse presses into your groin for twenty minutes," joked the surgeon, to the amusement of the on-looking crowd.

Surprisingly, I was never much concerned. After all, if you are going to bleed profusely, where better than in a hospital surrounded by doctors and nurses. Somebody asked how I was feeling and I replied, "Oh, I'm quite relaxed." I was as much an observer as everyone else.

Forty minutes after the line had been removed they released the pressure being applied in order to check on progress. Thankfully, all was well. The panic was over, the crowd dispersed and, after some partial sponging off of dried blood, my dignity was eventually restored.

FROM:	FIONA MAGGS
DATE:	10 FEBRUARY 2007
TO:	OUR NETWORK OF FRIENDS AND FAMILY
SUBJECT:	CHRIS IS HOME

At last I have got round to sitting down and writing an email to let you know that Chris was discharged from hospital on Thursday. We then had to go back on Friday for respiratory tests and were able to experience the snowy journey home yesterday afternoon. It was slow and I was very grateful for our four wheel drive car. We bought it two years ago to tow the caravan but that is a job that it has never had to do yet. Chris is still not 100% but feeling much better although he still has a chesty cough. He has a couple more tests booked for next week and one that needs changing as it is in March and that will be too late! I am hoping now for four days with no trips to Coventry.

Thank you to everyone who continues to pray and send encouraging messages to us. The next few weeks are going to be really tough and Chris is anxious about the next lot of treatment. Some of the side effects sound pretty unpleasant and he will get a sore mouth and throat and that will make eating and drinking difficult. I also think that boredom will be a big problem as just the couple of days in this week he found frustrating - although I did point out that next time he will feel much more ill, so maybe he will not notice!!

Fiona

WRITING WRONGS

I have just checked our calendar to see what else was going on around this time in terms of family life. It's all very well me going off for holidays in hospital and Fiona reorganising her life around me but the kids have routines to get on with too. Tim, of course, was more detached now that he lived in Portsmouth. Fiona did broach the subject with him once, to see if his concerns over his dad might be affecting him in any way. "No," says Tim, considering it seemingly for the first time. "When I'm at Uni. I don't really think about you at all." At least he's honest!

With Tim away, Luke became the oldest child and we noticed how grown up he was becoming. He coped really well with his school work, had an active involvement in our church youth group and was developing his own sense of identity. Luke had often asked about getting contact lenses, ostensibly for sport but I suspect also to reduce the frequent comments about how much he looked like his bespectacled dad. We had relented at last and February saw Luke taking ownership of a supply for occasional use. Personally, I've never had the desire to attach things to my eyeballs, in fact quite the opposite, and I was not surprised that initially it took Luke some time to put his lenses in. When he did though, it gave him quite another look. He reminded me of Peter Parker from the Spiderman films but I guess even that's better than looking like your dad.

Hannah was growing up fast too. In her last year at junior school she had developed a good set of close friends and was proving very capable in her work. She had the confidence to go to a Monday night science club held at the local senior school, even though she was the only girl from her school. She liked to walk to school and back by herself, though part of this was the embarrassment of having a dad with uncool hair. (As an aside, when writing this in October, having re-grown my hair but keeping it fairly short, she tells me I have more hair now than all of her friends' dads. Rather sadly I admit that made me feel quite proud, though I'm still in denial about the alleged bald patch at the back.) I got to spend more time talking to Hannah than with the boys because we nearly always read the Bible and prayed together at night. Her faith that God was in control and would look after us never faltered and this was an encouragement to me too.

Fiona had a rare evening out around this time as well. She went to see one of her favourite authors, Sophie Kinsella, with a friend. Sophie has written an amusing fictional series about a woman with an extensive shopping appetite and Fiona can relate to the urges if not the obsessive practice. She said it was interesting to see an author in the flesh and realise just how normal looking they are (no disrespect to Sophie)! Although, what an author might look like if not normal was not exactly clear. When I think about it, my own stereotype of what authors probably ought to look like involves glasses, slightly dishevelled hair and a rather withdrawn, shy manner. Salman Rushdie fits the bill rather well, though in his case being withdrawn may have something to do with the fatwa.

This reminds me again of my own pretensions to authorship. During my slow recovery in 2006 I managed to finish off a fictional novel I'd started writing many years ago and had added to occasionally since. They say there's a novel in every one of us, though they don't say whether it's any good or even worth writing down! My attempt revolved around the idea of the action hero dying in the first chapter, leaving the other characters somewhat nonplussed as to how to proceed. Not exactly mainstream storytelling but I liked the idea of the characters having to make their own way in a confusing situation – a metaphor for life perhaps.

It was a laborious process, though I am fortunate to be happy working on my own for hours on end. In fact, once I'm 'in the zone', as they say, time flies by. Even so, there were occasions when I lost the plot, quite literally, or struggled to remember which characters had said what, where they'd been, what they knew and so on. You have to know the thing inside out to be consistent and I confess that by the time I eventually re-edited it for the last time I had had more than enough. Imagine reading the same book repeatedly for months and still trying to be excited by it. At least when I was writing it for the first time I had no idea how it would end. (Why do schools take the thrill out of story writing by insisting on a full storyline set out in advance?) By the umpteenth read through it was so familiar I was quite happy to leave it alone and never see it again.

The next job was to trawl through the Writers' and Artists' Yearbook selecting literary agents who might be interested in representing me. I had to come up with a compelling synopsis that would sell the thing to them. It was difficult given how stale the whole thing seemed to me at the time. Over a period of months I sent off a selection of chapters for consideration. Each batch would return in dribs and drabs with the same reassuring messages that although they did not feel this was the right book for them I should keep trying.

It was what I had expected. After all, many great and successful writers have referred to this process and the fact that they were rejected many times before breaking through. What they don't say is that many more unsuccessful writers experience the same rejection and never break through! And of course, unsuccessful writers don't get interviewed or write articles about not getting published, or if they do nobody ever prints them.

So my dream of making a living by being an author remains a dream. It is some comfort though to have been able to write about my experiences on this cancer journey. The possibility of it being 'out there' and available for anyone to read is quite exciting. I like the idea that people I don't know could pick it up and hopefully enjoy it. What's more, it's a permanent record of the events and feelings we went through as a family; something we can refer back to in years to come. It may be fanciful but I like to imagine that my grandchildren's grandchildren might read this some day and understand the sort of people we were. If you are, then here's a message from the past just for you – "sorry about the genes". Oh, and never forget the God who made you and who can journey with you, through life and death and beyond.

FROM:	**FIONA MAGGS**
DATE:	**17 FEBRUARY 2007**
TO:	**OUR NETWORK OF FRIENDS AND FAMILY**
SUBJECT:	**ANOTHER WEEK GONE BY**

We have got through another week although it has not been without incident. We spent a long time at the hospital on Wednesday and managed to get all the tests needed completed on that day. My understanding of the workings of the NHS and persistence enabled us to get the March appointment moved. I overheard the receptionist at cardiac investigations saying "I have Mrs Maggs here and she wants the appointment this week" as if I were an awkward customer. I wanted to point out that it actually was the Consultant not me who wanted the investigation done quickly!!

We filled our time in-between various blood tests and visits to departments sitting in the new out-patients department on the comfortable chairs reading our books. I did wonder if at some point we would be noticed and asked to leave as it was over a five hour period that we kept coming and going. The new department is very spacious, clean and there is lots of light. Ideal for reading!

We repeated the experience on Thursday although were in a different department. This time we were going in for Chris to have his Hickman line fitted ready for next week's chemo and subsequent transplant. This meant a trip to theatre with the surgeon who we had previously met last week when Chris tried to bleed to death. This surgeon, like many others, is excellent at his job but somewhat lacking in people skills! He came and saw us and did all the necessary paperwork and then said he would send for Chris although he had a couple of other cases to do first. It was four and a quarter hours later that Chris was eventually taken to theatre.

He was then gone more than two hours and I was beginning to wonder if they would ever bring him back. As you might guess there was difficulty getting the line in. No pain this time as the local anaesthetic was very good but apparently the veins in Chris's chest have been damaged by the lymphoma and so the surgeon had difficulty getting the line in and to the correct place. After an x-ray we discovered that the staff were not very happy with the positioning but by that time it was 8.30pm and nothing else was going to happen, so we came home. They have decided that they will sort out the line on Tuesday when he is readmitted for his chemo so we wait to see what they decide to do.

We got home at nearly ten o'clock. Another long day at Coventry. It is only four weeks since we had the news that more treatment was needed and I have worked out that I have done nearly 1000 miles in that time. It would normally take me months to do that.

So everything is now ready for the next stage which should start on Tuesday. Again we have to phone to check that there is a bed. The ward is always very busy and all the beds full so we need a few people to go home in the next few days and there to be no emergency admissions. Please pray for Chris as he faces what is going to be a big challenge to him both physically and mentally. Also pray that the cough that he has not been able to get rid of now for nearly two weeks would disappear. They think it is viral as he has had numerous blood and sputum tests and there is no infection there. It is just annoying and makes lying on his back a problem.

Anyway I seem to have gone on rather a lot. My apologies if it is too much detail. Once again, thank you for your concern and prayers.

With much love, Fiona

BE PREPARED!

Many years ago our family were heavily involved in performing short dramatic presentations with a Christian message at various events. One of these was a modern re-telling of Jesus' story about some bridesmaids. As was the tradition in Israel, the bridesmaids were with the bride at her family home waiting for the bridegroom to come and fetch her. He might arrive at any time of the day or night. As night drew in, five of the bridesmaids made sure the oil in their lamps was topped up while the others did not. As a result, only five were ready to greet the bridegroom when he appeared.

Our sketch took the title 'Be Prepared' and featured two newspaper reporters waiting at an airport for the arrival of a famous movie star. Ronald was a suave, sophisticated man of the world, supremely confident in his own ability. He looked down on his nervous and untidy counterpart, Lawrence. But Lawrence's redeeming feature was his desire to do a good job, evidenced by his attention to detail. While Ronald naturally assumed everything would run smoothly, Lawrence constantly checked his pencil was sharp, his notebook ready and his camera loaded. Needless to say, it was Lawrence who got the scoop interview and pictures when the delayed movie star turned up unexpectedly and Ronald discovered he had no film left.

The point of Jesus' story is to be ready to meet your maker and it was with this in the back of my mind that I made some preparations for the forthcoming highly intensive treatment I was about to undergo. Basically, it involved poisoning my body, wiping out my immune system, then waiting for me to recover – a bit like wiping the hard disc on a computer and re-installing the system.

We'd been talking about making a will for years. In fact, I had gone so far as entering the premises of a solicitor on the High Street once to make enquiries. The place looked modern and attractive and the smiling receptionist was friendly. However, she directed me out of the door to another building further down the street where they dealt with 'personal' clients. Apparently the attractive building I was in was only for 'commercial' clients.

There was a marked difference in the character of this other building. It was much older, less well fitted out and the receptionist somewhat less pleased to see me. I was directed to a waiting area where I perused the adverts for their services until a flustered solicitor bustled out to see me. I assume they must have a lot of enquiries that never turn into business as she gave the impression that it was all a bit of an inconvenience and she'd rather be getting on with some proper work.

She ran through the basics, which consisted of telling me I could have a cheap and cheerful standard will if I wasn't worth much but if I had any assets to speak of it would be complicated because of inheritance tax. I was given some prices and shown the door. I never went back.

It was late in 2006 that I started thinking about it again. This time I tried exploring possibilities over the internet. There are loads of sites to investigate and, as is my usual internet experience, I followed several blind alleys that took me nowhere. Offers of free, do-it-yourself wills turned out to be hopelessly inadequate and the cut-price will market lacked the reassuring professional touch. In desperation, I emailed one of the friendlier looking solicitors for help. The literature they sent me was very readable and, although complicated, I at last had the impression that they wanted our business. And so I agreed to launch into the unknown with them.

The first job, it turned out, was to complete a form listing all our worldly wealth. I confess, I quite liked it. With my natural instinct for paperwork and record keeping I enjoyed gathering all the data and collating a spreadsheet. Then it was a question of adding it all up to see what I was worth, or, more pertinently, allowing for life assurance policies what I was worth dead! It is a little sobering to see your life summed up by a figure with a pound sign at the front but there was no space on the form to add my many other qualities and achievements. If it couldn't be sold for cash, it didn't count.

I could not resist going on from there to work out what would happen if I died first, if Fiona died first and if we both died simultaneously. I couldn't come up with any other permutations to play around with but I ran through all of these scenarios both with and without an inheritance-tax-saving will. Honestly, there's a lot of fun to be had contemplating your own mortality – or is that just me?

The other 'asset' we had to consider was our children. The form asked who we would like to appoint as guardians. It was an interesting question. Who would we want to care for our children? Or to put it the other way around, who would really want the job? It prompted a good discussion about standards and spiritual values; about what was really important to us – a refreshing change after all the figures. I cannot remember whether or not we said anything to the people we eventually put down. If not, it could be a nice surprise for them!

Having sent this information off, we got back a letter from the solicitors enclosing the first draft of our wills. It was dated 11 January 2007, the date we found out that the tumour was still active and further treatment was needed. It was a good way of sharpening our focus on the task in hand. So, with the possibility of extinction looming in my mind, I reviewed the documents, made a few changes and sent them back.

To sign the final versions we went into the solicitors' offices in Birmingham on 12 February. The building had that comfortable feeling of formal opulence that solicitors seem to get away with, despite the knowledge that they have built up their wealth by taking money from their clients. Perversely, their occupation of modern facilities in high-rise buildings overlooking the heart of the city assures you that the fee you are paying is money well spent. But the man we dealt with was very friendly and down-to-earth and did not mention money at all. In fact, we brought it up right at the end of our visit as it seemed impolite not to.

Other preparations for this second hospital visit involved packing things to keep me amused during weeks of isolation, since this stay would be longer and lonelier than any before. First was my trusty Puzzler (a 2005 issue which must have been left over from last year's recuperations). Second, a couple of modern hi-tech gadgets I had purchased for my previous incarceration. One was a portable DVD player. I imagined the prolonged solitude would be the perfect time to take in a range of films, comedy programmes and dramas we had accumulated or borrowed for the occasion. The other was an MP3 player.

Now, to the younger generation, an MP3 player may not even qualify as either modern or hi-tech but to a man of my advancing years it remained something of a mystery. I knew the concept involved holding lots of music on a small stick but how it got there was still a mystery to me. Taking a step back, it was a mystery to me why you'd want to put a lot of music on a small stick at all. I was happy to listen to music on the radio sometimes when in the car or at home but the idea of having it follow me around wherever I went and whatever I was doing seemed like a nightmare. I like a clear (some would say empty) head. Forcing it to reverberate to the beat of non-stop music sounded like a form of torture.

Nevertheless, during my hospital stays I had thought the occasional bit of music would be soothing. So, what to buy? The range of gadgetry was mind blowing. Some of it looked like pure science fiction, had the capacity to accommodate every song ever written and cost an arm and a leg. Fortunately, Tesco had a special offer MP3 for £4.99. That would do for me.

Of course, I had to get Luke to show me how to load it with music from my CDs. Actually, when I say 'show me' I admit he was sitting at the computer and pressing all the buttons but at least I was in the room overseeing the process. I think it only took about six albums but that was fine. Being a basic model it did not have many features or buttons and the operation was supposed to be 'intuitive'. I think that means they don't bother to explain it to you. Anyway, all I needed was to know how to turn it on and how to turn it off. At least, that's what I thought. More on that shortly.

A final preparation was on more of a spiritual line. Having the whole day with nothing particular to do sounds great but I knew I could easily become lethargic and apathetic, especially once the effects of the treatment kicked in. My good intentions of spending time with God in meditation and prayer could easily slide. So I wanted to introduce a little structure into the day. I turned to the Northumbrian Office, a routine of morning, midday and evening meditations in the Celtic tradition. From what I understood, finding God both in periods of isolation and in the daily routine was part of the Celtic approach. I somehow identified my hospital isolation with the Celtic monks going to their simple cells and wanted my room to become for me a place of prayer.

It was also a way of connecting with many friends who were supporting me through prayer during this time. By letting them know what I was doing they were able to participate in the same thoughts and meditations as me in their daily routines. It proved very comforting and powerful, as I'll explain later.

So, with my physical, mental and spiritual equipment all packed, I felt I was ready to take the next step of the journey.

FROM:	FIONA MAGGS
DATE:	20 FEBRUARY 2007
TO:	OUR NETWORK OF FRIENDS AND FAMILY
SUBJECT:	ADMITTED AS PLANNED

Chris went into hospital today. The bed was ready at 8.30am. Chris was not! He was still in bed and had gone back to sleep so had to drag himself out and off we went.

Nothing to report about today. Just a few blood tests, lots of questions and hours of lounging around. The chemo starts tomorrow although the staff are still 'discussing' what to do about the line. The doctors and the nurses do not seem to be agreeing at the moment so we wait to see what the outcome is. The line may be changed but I think they are just going to put in a normal cannula for the chemo tomorrow. The bad news is that there is a diarrhoea and sickness bug at the hospital and so they have imposed strict visiting restrictions, only one visitor per day and only between 7 - 8pm. This is a whole hospital policy although some wards are closed completely to visitors. The good news is that the bug has not been on Ward 34 where Chris is but obviously I will not be able to see much of him so he is going to be spending even more time alone than expected.

That's all for now.
Love Fiona

HEAVENS ABOVE

Staying in a single room in a hospital day after day gives you plenty of time for thinking. Not everyone's cup of tea, but as an introvert I'm quite content inside my own head and tend to spend a lot of time there even in normal circumstances. Given the purpose of my stay I got to thinking a little about heaven. My Christian faith has taught me that there's not just life after death but life more abundant and fulfilling than anything we can experience here and now. But what does that mean? Ah, now, that's the question.

Taking a step backwards first of all, I should say that talking about heaven is fraught with difficulty. Most of us have some concept of heaven, built up over years of mixed up images and fanciful ideas, mostly involving people with feathery wings and Persil-white robes floating blissfully in a cloudy paradise with benign and somewhat sickly smiles on their faces. I imagine most of us would also recognise this as 'Hollywood Heaven' – a stereotype developed over the ages in art, films and on TV as a kind of shorthand for the general principle of life after death (and fairly cheap to reproduce with the odd smoke machine covering over a multitude of sins, so to speak). But if you said to people, "No, really, what do you think heaven is like?" I suspect most of us have very little idea.

As a regular church attendee throughout my childhood, I was very familiar with the teaching that believers will go to heaven when they die. As I came to develop my own understanding of Christian faith and made a decision to base my life on the foundation of Jesus' teaching and sacrificial redemption, the prospect of heaven remained a firm part of my big picture of the meaning of life. But what I find truly awe-inspiring about being a follower of Jesus is the fact that we are always learners; discovering deeper truths and new perspectives on God the more we look. Faith is dynamic – a living, developing kaleidoscope of experiences and insights. So perhaps it should not have surprised me (though it did) when I began to realise fairly recently that my understanding of heaven was possibly well short of its reality.

I suppose I used to think of heaven as 'somewhere else'. I mean, where we are now – the reality we know around us physically – is clearly not heaven, is it. Heaven is where God is fully known, fully revealed, fully glorified, fully worshipped and his perfect ways are fully followed. As the Lord's Prayer says, "May your kingdom come, may your will be done, on earth as it is in heaven." I understood heaven to be God's separate kingdom. As to where it was, precisely, I had no idea. I never bought into the idea of it being part of our physical universe – established in a galaxy just to the left of Alpha Centauri, for example. I imagined it totally outside of the physical realm and therefore clearly separate – another dimension or a parallel universe perhaps. It wasn't particularly important where it was, I just knew it was a place where believers would go after death and it was perfect.

My thinking now is rather different, and still, I admit, under development. The big difference lies in the proximity of heaven. Perhaps it is not 'somewhere else', it is everywhere. And everywhere, by definition, includes right here around and about me. I find it a difficult thing to grasp, let alone explain. In my first go at writing this piece I included a rambling attempt at doing so but Fiona, in her dutiful wifely way, gently pointed out that I was waffling and what I really needed to do was get back to the story. She's right. But anyone who shows the remotest interest in this subject in my presence finds me more than willing to indulge in further discussion.

Meanwhile, back in the hospital, the second batch of chemotherapy was even worse than the first. Known as BEAM, it included one drug referred to as the 'Domestos' of chemo, aiming to wipe out everything in its path. So more drips, boluses and all the attendant side effects again.

It's difficult to describe what those days were like in any detail. My energy levels were very low and I had no enthusiasm to record the events as they happened. A picture Fiona took of me lying in bed, half asleep and sporting a foolish grin, sums up how I felt inside too. When I was conscious it was a lazy consciousness that knew what was going on but took little interest in being an active part of it. Medical treatment makes you very passive anyway – it tends to be done *to* you. When that treatment knocks you back like chemo does, you have little choice but to lie back and let it run its course. Some of the glimpses I had of other patients on the ward suggested they had blanked out altogether, gazing expressionlessly at a TV screen for most of the day.

There was comfort in knowing that it would not last forever. I had been given a table listing the daily regime and it was always pleasurable to be able to tick off another section and appreciate that the end was nearer.

I remember one dose of a particular drug that had a surprising effect. The nurse that gave it to me warned me it might create an unusual tingling sensation as she had had it herself when she was ill. However, I was not prepared for what happened about ten seconds after the drug hit my bloodstream. There was the most intense pins and needles experience in my nether regions that had me writhing about clutching my buttocks together for about a minute or so. Whether the drug had any medicinal purposes I don't know but as a recreational activity I would highly recommend it.

To give you a sense of the state of mind I was in, one of my frequent diversions was to watch the temperature on my fridge. Each room had its own fridge and on the door was a digital record of the internal temperature, which the nurses had to check every now and then. The thermostat would register when the temperature rose above a certain level and this would trigger the refrigeration unit to kick in with a loud humming, bringing the reading down again. Many a happy twenty minutes was spent observing the gradual increase in temperature, slow at first and then increasing in speed. Every 0.1 of a degree was observed and the excitement built to a crescendo as the reading got closer to the maximum allowed. The anticipation of the fridge juddering into action once more was only exceeded by the thrill of seeing the numbers tumble down once the refrigeration unit was fully working. And then, quite suddenly, the noise would stop. But still the temperature dropped, as if in freefall for a few seconds, before slowing, levelling off and eventually beginning its next ascent.

Strangely, the exact temperatures at which the fridge turned on and off were rarely the same and could differ markedly from day to day, which of course kept me on the edge of my bed and made the whole thing even more interesting than you can imagine.

What else can I remember about the room? Well, several things did not work. These included the bathroom lock, the curtains (which fell sadly short of covering the window) and the 'on' button on my bed's remote control. Like most of the beds in the hospital I could, in theory, adjust the slope and height of the bed, with the top and bottom halves having separate functions. So I could, if necessary, fold the bed in half, though preferably not with me in it. This range of movement was very useful for the rigours of the day such as sitting up to eat, lying back to read and lying flat to sleep. However, to get my remote control device turned on, I had to get out from under the covers and press a button at the bottom of the bed. I suppose the exercise did me some good.

The other thing that did not work was the taps at the sink in the bathroom. They were covered over with a big yellow bag displaying a warning not to use them for fear of infection. When I moved in I assumed this was a temporary state of affairs but after three days or so, when nobody had done anything about it, I plucked up the nerve to ask when it might be fixed. The nurse just looked at me pityingly. Apparently things rarely get fixed and the notion that the nurses might know when such a miracle would occur was clearly misguided.

When I eventually left, after three weeks or so, nothing had changed, and for all I know it is still there today. The one thing that did get immediate attention was the in-house entertainment system. Even though I had not subscribed to it, my clinical 'isolation' had to be violated by a technician when my room's TV/telephone/internet system needed a software upgrade. Priorities, priorities, priorities.

FROM:	FIONA MAGGS
DATE:	1 MARCH 2007
TO:	OUR NETWORK OF FRIENDS AND FAMILY
SUBJECT:	UPDATE ON CHRIS

Ten days have now gone past since his admission and Chris has had all his chemotherapy and on Tuesday evening his stem cells were given back to him. He did have a few days of sickness but that was controlled with more anti- sickness drugs.

Unfortunately the Hickman line did not work - it leaked into his chest when they tried it out - so it was removed on Saturday morning in theatre. He has had another line put in his arm which so far is still working although they are now not able to get any blood from it. This means he is having daily blood taken from his hands or arms - not an easy task. On Monday they had nine attempts! Nobody did one on Tuesday and Chris just kept quiet (I reckoned nobody was brave enough to try!) Wednesday was only three attempts. He is quite swollen from all the fluids that he has been given so that makes the job more difficult.

Apart from the fact that he is not keen to let them get at his blood Chris is not too bad at the moment. He is very weak and spending a lot of his time sleeping which passes the time. Over the next few days he will become neutropenic and the more intensive isolation rules will come into effect. Unfortunately due to the hospital cutting visiting he has had an enforced isolation with only me being able to visit him (although I have been allowed in for longer than the official times).

We now have a couple more weeks where the chemo is working and the stem cells are making their way to the bone marrow and 'grafting' and starting to produce new cells. The staff on the ward are all really lovely and friendly and do make the whole experience less traumatic.

We do thank everyone for their prayers and messages. Over the next few weeks Chris will be more at risk of infection and although we do expect some minor problems we would ask you to pray for protection from anything major. We are looking forward to Chris being at home again and a reduction of trips to Coventry!

Thank you
Love from Fiona

SOLITARY CONFINEMENT

After the thrill of having my stem cells harvested some weeks earlier through a machine that looked like something out of a 1970's Bond film, I was keen to see how the process worked in reverse. I was also keen to have my stem cells back because, if my limited grasp of the process was correct, I would die without them. These stem cells were the means by which my immune system would be kick-started again after the devastation of the chemotherapy treatment. Their return would also mean the end of days of being on a drip and the thought of independent movement was very appealing, even though I would not be able to go anywhere, apart from the en-suite bathroom, for weeks.

To mark the occasion, Fiona dressed up. She wore my favourite dress; one that I had actually picked out for her during a shopping trip together some time before. She had been looking for something for a wedding and, as most women will know, the process is always incredibly complex. Over a period of many weeks, several dresses had been considered and rejected – too short, too long, too dull, too bright, too big, too small, too summery, too heavy, too risqué, too matronly, too tight around the hips, too loose around the bust. I confess, my enthusiasm for the process had waned long ago. But for some reason, probably during a recuperation period when my resistance was weakened, I had been persuaded to accompany Fiona on another expedition to the 'ladieswear' jungle. Anyway, it was me who pulled out this particular dress and suggested it might do the job. Surprisingly (most of my suggestions get short shrift) Fiona tried it on and was pleased with the result. And I thought she looked stunning in it – both at the wedding and sitting by my hospital bed.

The stem cells were delivered to my room a few hours before the event, travelling in a large canister. They remained frozen inside the canister, which was filled with some sort of gas. At the appointed time, two of the senior nurses, one of whom was the ward manager, came to do the transplant. There was lots of preparation and double-checking before the canister was opened, with a hiss and a waft of gas. The nurse wore what looked like heavy-duty gardening gloves because the contents were frozen. She carefully pulled out a rather stiff, sorry looking bag of frozen yellow mush. It occurred to me that if she dropped it – not so unlikely given the clumsy nature of the gloves – my precious stem cell collection would shatter into a thousand pieces.

The nurses then proceeded to defrost the bag using warm water. It could have been sweetcorn soup they were getting ready for lunch. Actually, the similarity with sweetcorn extended beyond the colour. Apparently the solution in which the stem cells are held has a strong smell which is similar to sweetcorn and this would permeate through my body for a number of days. I never smelled it because I was in the room all the time but anyone entering from outside could tell.

And then, in a somewhat disappointing anticlimax, the defrosted bag was hooked up to my drip and the contents seeped their way into my system over a couple of hours without much ceremony. The only significant difference was that the two nurses had to remain with me throughout the process, so they and Fiona had a good old chinwag about all sorts of unrelated topics while I lay smiling lamely and gradually adopted the odour of sweetcorn. The full pictorial record is in Fiona's scrapbooking album – but without the smells.

And so began the long wait and more intense isolation period. As my immunity would be extremely low for at least two weeks I was allowed only one visitor a day. Fiona made it most days and my Dad substituted when she could not. It was not exactly solitary confinement, especially with so many hospital staff in and out, but there certainly was a dearth of meaningful human contact.

Much of the time was spent sleeping or dozing or sitting staring blankly at the wall in a lazy state of mental inactivity. If I got bored occasionally, and I rarely did, it was not through lack of things to do but a lack of energy or enthusiasm to do them. I made occasional trips to the small window, especially when it was sunny, to watch the world go by. In this context, the world consisted largely of the comings and goings of construction contractors situated in a temporary building at the back of the hospital. Not the most enthralling of views but it reassured me to know that life was carrying on.

At some stage I wrote this little poem, which gives a flavour of the days drifting by and a sense of God somehow suffering alongside me.

Confined
Four walls, long days, slow nights,
A simple life of maintenance.

Small routines to give purpose to the day,
Left to contemplate my mortality
Or escape in stories to unreal worlds.
But he is here
And that makes all the difference.

One of my main distractions was my DVD player. This was the perfect opportunity to watch a film or two a day – something which, in normal circumstances, I would have relished. It worked pretty well at first, though I don't think I ever got through a whole film without hitting the pause button for a blood test, change of bed, room cleaning, drug round, doctor's visit, cup of tea, a meal or to have my blood pressure taken. Sometimes it seemed like all of them at the same time. But once the effects of the chemotherapy started to bite, my concentration levels were so poor I found even watching a DVD too intense and preferred just gazing blankly at the opposite wall. When my son, Luke, heard this he was appalled. He simply could not imagine feeling so unwell that you could not watch a DVD!

The MP3 player was a less intense amusement and I started to use it in an evening as a means of relaxing before going to sleep. On the first such occasion it was great, listening to a selection of my favourite music and watching the little red light on the gadget flash on and off. After about half an hour though, instead of the next track there was a click followed by silence. I looked at the little black stick, waiting for it to tell me what was wrong. It didn't. So I pressed a button or two and eventually got it to play the same track again, after which it clicked and went off. I'd had enough for that evening anyway so I left it and went to sleep.

The next evening I tried again. Everything seemed to work perfectly, for a while. But again, at some point it refused to play a track and just clicked off. I made more of an effort to work out how to control the sequence but there were only two buttons and my haphazard poking at them seemed to produce entirely random effects. I think I managed to return to the beginning and listened to the same tracks again but I knew there was a lot more music on it that I just could not access.

I made several attempts over the next few days to control the mini-monster but could never master it. I ended up being more frustrated by it than relaxed and gave it up altogether. I thought I would sort it out when I got back home (with Luke's help) but I never have. And while I'm at it I might as well admit I've never listened to a podcast, have never been on facebook and have no idea what bluetooth even means. But still, somehow, I seem to live a contented life.

I mentioned earlier my intention to use the Northumbrian Office (a set of morning, midday and evening readings and meditations from the Christian Celtic tradition) during my stay in hospital to give some spiritual routine to the day. I'm pleased to say that I stuck to it 'religiously'. Generally I hate the word 'religious' – it conjures up in my mind pious rituals and hypocritical legalism. But on this occasion, forcing myself to follow a set programme made sure I applied myself to the things of God when my human instinct would have been not to bother. When I would have struggled to find words of my own, the words of others supported me.

Okay, I confess I did not always find strength and inspiration. Sometimes it felt like I was just reading the words without any real meaning. But other times there were expressions and passages that really connected with my circumstances. One particular section that I read every evening spoke directly to my tired spirit.

Lord, You have always given
Bread for the coming day,
And though I am poor,
    Today I believe.

Lord, You have always given
Strength for the coming day,
And though I am weak,
    Today I believe.

Lord, You have always given
Peace for the coming day,
And though of anxious heart,
    Today I believe.

Lord, You have always kept
Me safe in trials,
And now, tried as I am,
    Today I believe.

Lord, You have always marked
The road for the coming day,
And though it may be hidden,
    Today I believe.

Lord, You have always lightened
This darkness of mine,
And though the night is here,
    Today I believe.

Lord, You have always spoken
When time was ripe,
And though You be silent now,
    Today I believe.

Some of our friends and family had committed to follow the same readings over this period. Knowing that others were sharing the routine with me, as they were able, gave me spiritual companionship. They were with me 'in spirit' in a way that I do not fully understand but believe to be entirely real. And I am confident that as they stood alongside me in this way God blessed them too through the words and thoughts we shared.

FROM:	FIONA MAGGS
DATE:	13 MARCH 2007
TO:	OUR NETWORK OF FRIENDS AND FAMILY
SUBJECT:	CHRIS IS HOME

After 22 days Chris has returned home feeling very tired and weak but very happy to get out of his hospital room. The doctors decided yesterday that if his blood results today were ok they would let him go. He has been managing without any intravenous antibiotics, platelets or fluids since Sunday morning when his cannula came out and they were unable, after a number of attempts, to get another line in.

Unfortunately the mid line that he had in his left arm for most of his treatment stopped working last Thursday and he has now got a blood clot in that arm (a repeat of what happened in his right arm during 2005) and so he will be on anti-coagulants for a while again. After that stopped working they did have trouble getting cannulas in that worked (even tried to put them in his feet - six attempts that all failed). He is enjoying experiencing all the comforts of home, sitting in a comfy chair and sleeping in his own bed (was there after a short time back in the house!).

He is back to the hospital on Thursday morning for more blood tests to check that everything is as it should be. It will take him some time to get his energy back and be able to start doing things again.

Thanks again to all of you who have been praying for us and supporting us in other ways.

Love Fiona

EVERYBODY NEEDS SOME BODY

Aren't bodies great? Take a look at yours. It's an amazing piece of equipment. One of its most incredible aspects is its capacity to heal itself. A cut will generally bleed but the bleeding process automatically triggers a clotting mechanism to stem the flow. Brilliant! Who thought of that? If a virus gets into your system there are millions of cells specifically there to deal with it And the body works as a whole unit by concentrating on priority areas. So when you need all your energy to fight off infection, other parts temporarily close down. You retire to bed, often sleeping. Even your conscious mind, which we tend to think of as the real 'me', gets sidelined as our body instinctively works on the top priority.

As I recovered from the damage caused by chemotherapy treatment my body somehow knew what to do. Nobody needed to explain the process to it, or list the restoration sequence that should take place, it was all in hand somewhere in my body's make-up. The medical fraternity has made great strides in its understanding over the centuries but much of it has been simply observing what the body does itself and creating the best environment for it to do its work. In a sense, I trust my body more than I trust my own thoughts.

If that last sentence sounds a little odd, think about it. We all know that our perceptions can be deceived by, say, optical illusions. But even when you know you are being deceived, because the illusion has been explained to you, you still see the illusion because the evidence of your eyes is what you have learned to trust. Seeing is believing, as they say.

I love the way we do things with our bodies without being conscious of it. Body language is a good example. Our facial expressions, hand gestures, posture, even where we position ourselves relative to someone else are all sub-conscious activities. Sometimes we can override them with conscious thought and action but try keeping it up for any period and it's exhausting.

Then there are those moments of instinctive reaction that again seem to bypass conscious thought. I'm not thinking of physical reactions, though there are plenty of those, but mental responses such as angry retorts, impatient snappy remarks or shouts of encouragement at a crucial moment in a sporting event. Part of the brain operates what is effectively our character without bothering to refer everything through the 'Executive Board' of consciousness. It is slightly alarming to realise that the majority of my behaviour happens without me thinking it through.

Language is another fascinating aspect of this. Writing this down now I am thinking fairly clearly about what to say, and if I don't think it sounds right I can delete it and rewrite what I want. I make sure it is structured, with punctuation and grammatical rules being followed as well as I can. The end result is a very consciously thought out communication. Language in general speech is quite different though. We learn from a young age to turn thoughts into words very quickly. Most of the time in conversation we find words flow without careful preparation and 'choosing our words carefully' is an expression we quite rightly reserve for unusual and specific circumstances.

In conversations we don't worry about sentence structure much at all and punctuation is entirely absent. Even over the telephone we can easily convey meaning through varying emphasis, occasional noises ("mmm") and timing (momentary hesitations often speaking louder than words). And most of this all gets processed sub-consciously. Sometimes it's as if we hear our own words at the same time as everyone else, even though they are expressing our own thoughts. How often do we think, "I shouldn't have said that", after it has come out?

Sometimes I get to wondering where I stop and my body starts. After all, I would still be me if I had to have a leg removed. How much of my body could I do without? Science fiction has played around with the concept of a brain being kept alive after a body has died, or even transplanted into another body. I quite like the idea, though I wouldn't want to try it myself. It seems to me that the relationship between a brain and a body is so individual that waking up in someone else's body would be like wearing shoes that didn't fit – and not being able to take them off.

No, I'll stick to my own rather battered and worn body for the moment. It has served me well enough over the years, and it carries the scars that remind me of what I've been through. I was going to say I've grown accustomed to my own face but, actually, that's one aspect of my body I don't know so well. I exist behind my face and only get to see it in mirrors (the image always reversed left to right). So I probably have quite a distorted view.

Occasionally, when I'm shaving and get up quite close to the mirror, I find the intimate detail of my facial features quite alarming. It is as if I am looking closely at someone else entirely. Or is that just me?

FROM:	**FIONA MAGGS**
DATE:	**2 MAY 2007**
TO:	**OUR NETWORK OF FRIENDS AND FAMILY**
SUBJECT:	**SIX WEEKS ON!**

I have been intending to send an update for the last week but I only seem to remember when I have switched the computer off for the night. That happened again today but we have switched back on so that the deed can be done!

Last Tuesday Chris had a follow up appointment with the Consultant Oncologist at Coventry to check up on how he is doing. They are pleased with his progress and although he is still a little anaemic his bone marrow is slowly building up to working as normal. We had a very long and frank discussion with the Doctor about the future and all the various possibilities and came away feeling that she had given us a very realistic picture.

At present they are arranging for a CT scan to be done at the end of May and Chris will then see the Doctor again in mid June. The CT scan will assess any damage to his lungs and also see what his veins are looking like after his various clots and difficulties with the lines. They will be following him up for at least another 5 years and it is very much waiting to see what happens. He has been told to take 3 months from his hospital discharge before he starts to return to work again which should be mid-

June. It will take a good 6 months for him to get back to normal (if we can remember what that is like).

My home rehabilitation programme for Chris has restarted with little jobs around the house interspersed with rests. He is also taking quite an active part at church as we are both now members of the leadership team again this year. It is quite amazing how well he is feeling considering what he had to go through just over two months ago. He is also pleased as his hair is just starting to grow back again. Not sure how long it will be until he gets a full head of hair (or the same bits back that he had before!).

The family are all well with Luke preparing for his GCSEs which start in a matter of weeks. Hannah also has her year 6 SATs tests very soon and Tim is in the last few weeks of his Uni term. He finishes on 8th June for the summer! So having got used to there being just the 4 of us we will be back to 5. Then in October he will go again and we will have to go through the adjustment all over again.

We have discovered on our journey that there are times of crisis followed by periods of relative calm. We are pleased to be in the latter at the moment but value your continued prayers as there are many uncertainties about the future.

With love from us all
Fiona

ALL HANDS TO THE PUMP!

May saw the introduction into our family of a new little member. It sleeps in our bed, requires regular attention and stays with Fiona on a virtually permanent basis. It is an insulin pump.

Fiona became an insulin dependent diabetic when she was 20 and has lived with the condition ever since. It is so much a part of our lives that we often forget that without regular injections of insulin she would die. She never makes a fuss about it and many of our friends would not even know. By consistent monitoring combined with a controlled diet she has kept at bay the deterioration in health that often accompanies the disease. With all my recent suffering it is easy to forget she has to cope with this condition day in, day out for the rest of her life. I think she is truly amazing.

At first, her insulin regime involved two injections a day. Treatment was relatively unsophisticated in the early 80s and she had to stick to regular eating times and amounts (measured in grams of carbohydrate). Being a recent diabetic she enjoyed what is commonly know as a 'honeymoon period' during which her blood sugar levels were not too difficult to control because her pancreas was still partially working. After a few years her pancreas was no longer assisting in blood sugar control and everything had to be managed by balancing carbohydrate intake and insulin injections.

Over the years, the growing sophistication of insulin types has allowed greater flexibility in diet but the constant monitoring always continues. It has meant more injections per day to get the right mix of insulin types and, with Fiona's body reacting differently over time, control has been very difficult at times. Her consultants have frequently been concerned about the number of times her blood sugar drops to dangerously low levels during the night. Fiona has got used to waking up feeling unwell and eating high-sugar foods in the dark while her dear husband sleeps blissfully by her side.

For a few years Fiona had been unhappy with the high blood sugars she was experiencing every morning. Various injection regimes had been tried and she was up to six or seven injections a day to manage the problem. An insulin pump is an alternative way of delivering the insulin to try and improve overall control. It involves inserting a line into her abdomen, through which a consistent flow of insulin can be delivered. The little black box at the other end of the line contains a reservoir of insulin, a battery and a control panel so that she can boost her insulin levels when she eats. The site where the line is inserted has to be moved every three days. Fiona does this with a clever little device that shoots both a needle and a line into her. The needle is withdrawn and the line is left secured by a small sticky dressing.

It has proved very successful. Her blood sugar levels have improved, though they are still subject to the occasional blip. You'd think having to carry the pump around with her would become a nuisance but she has adjusted quickly and only occasionally has the line been unceremoniously ripped from its place because she forgot the pump was clipped onto her trousers when she got undressed.

Unfortunately, clothing now has to be chosen to accommodate the pump. Close fitting tops with a big lump under them do not work. Neither do long, flowing ball gowns – but then again, as Fiona often points out, she has little opportunity to wear them. Waistbands need to be strong enough to hold the weight and the trend toward revealing your abdomen in public is also out. It has not meant a completely new wardrobe but 'one or two' extra purchases have been necessary.

So the pump has become one of the family. It joined us on our first family holiday for two years the week after Fiona got it. At the end of May we pulled out the old caravan, gave it a wash and brush up, and headed off to the delights of a field near Abingdon. It was the Caravanners and Campers' Christian Fellowship (CCCF) Spring Bank Holiday Rally. We have enjoyed being part of this event for many years but had missed it in 2005 and 2006 due to illness. My parents are caravanners too and they were camped next to us with my sister, Liz, and her two youngest boys.

It turned out to be a somewhat wet experience. I think it was dry when we arrived on the Friday afternoon but certainly by Saturday the rain came and it came to stay. Sunday we spent virtually the whole day inside our little aluminium and acrylic capped ABS cabin (I had to look that up in the brochure) trying to amuse ourselves with games while Luke manfully revised for his GCSEs. Tim was still away at University. By the Monday, when we had listened to the rain beating persistently on the part laminated roof and panoramic rooflight all night and into the morning, we called Fiona's sister in Swindon and asked if we could take refuge in her warm dry house for a few hours.

I've nothing against squelching through mud in Wellingtons, wearing a cagoule and waterproof trousers to try and keep out the determined rain and cold wind, pulling the empty water container along behind and then getting soaked at the water tap because the pipe comes off in your hand. After all, that's what camping is all about. But at Fiona's sister's house it was wonderful to sit on a real sofa, go to a solid toilet and take a shower without wondering if the water might run out (again) at any minute.

Usually on our caravan holidays, something within the van will go wrong. The fridge might be impossible to get going, the battery might drain away completely, there might even be a problem with the 'portaloo'. But by far and away the most frequent malfunctions involve the plumbing. As you can imagine, the plumbing in a caravan is not very complex. There is a water container outside, into which a pump is inserted. This draws water to taps in the kitchen and bathroom area and to the shower. What could go wrong? Well, over the years pretty much everything, but this holiday's excitement involved the kitchen tap deciding to leak water. We noticed a puddle on the surface around the taps first and on further investigation discovered it was only the tip of the iceberg (if that's not stretching the water-based analogy too far). The cupboard underneath was drenched and more water was coming through.

We immediately turned off the pump and soaked up the spillage. That was the easy bit. I then looked at it. Looking at things is my usual first instinct. I suppose I think that maybe, just one day, I'll see something and say, "Oh yes, it's just this", adjust a nut or some such and, hey presto, all will be well. It hasn't happened yet.

After looking for a bit I then start fiddling. This is when Fiona starts getting agitated. "Do you know what you're doing?" She knows I don't. I feign confidence and attempt a repair, more in hope than anything else. "Try it now," I say, in the manner of someone who's in the plumbing business. Water spurts everywhere and we resume the process of mopping up.

The annoying thing about caravans (you might argue it's just one among many) is that getting repairs done is such a pain.

Generally you have to take the problem to a caravan repair centre so that they can assess it and book it in for another day. Then you have to take it on the allocated day and go and get it back again when they've finished. So this involves three trips to and from the caravan repair centre, which is not close, plus all the hassle of hitching up at one end of the journey and unhitching at the other. My heart sank at the prospect of having to go through all this when we got back home. Plus there was the difficulty of getting through the rest of the holiday without running water.

CCCF has had a lot of experience in running rallies and is blessed with many skilled and helpful people who devote a large part of their holiday time to performing duties for the good of the whole. We had heard there was, on site, a Mr Fix-It. He had agreed to be on hand to help with any little difficulties people encountered.

We were told his pitch was in the far bottom corner of the field from us. When we found it, his car plus part of his awning was sitting in a small lake formed by the recent downpours, so it seemed he was facing a few trials of his own. He was not in when we knocked but his jolly wife assured us he would be able to call when he was free.

When he arrived I noticed, with some satisfaction, that he looked, then he fiddled (though his fiddling seemed to have somewhat more purpose about it). Before long the tap was off and he was attacking the top with a sharp screwdriver, convinced that the problem lay underneath a small plastic bit of trimming. I must admit, I had my doubts. I even wondered about asking him if he was sure. I'm glad I didn't. Despite this being a model of tap he told us he'd never encountered before he managed to work it out, fix it and replace it within ten minutes. He even attempted to explain to me what he'd done – something about counter-screwing the female widget socket I think. Anyway, we are eternally grateful to Mr Fix-It for saving the day, though I do wonder whether that was his real name.

The rain subsided a little on Tuesday and when we departed on Wednesday it was fairly dry. However, the heavy rain over several days had turned the makeshift roads on the site into mud tracks and nobody was allowed to use them. Exit from the field, we had been told, was only permitted with the assistance of one of the many 4x4 Land Rovers and the like on site, "unless you are sure you can get off by yourself". Confidence has always been one of my strengths – often unjustified confidence but confidence nevertheless. After all, I had a 4x4 Audi, albeit just an estate car, and we were not too far from the tarmac road running through the farm out of the site. I assured Fiona it would be fine.

So we said our goodbyes to my parents, got in the car and made for the road. To be fair, I nearly got there. The front wheels were only a matter of a couple of metres from the road. But a patch of soft soil, some might even say quicksand, had prevented us from getting all the way and now I sat, spinning wheels embedded in the earth, feeling rather foolish. I had to go and confess my arrogance to the team organising tow-outs and await assistance.

When help arrived I compounded my embarrassment by not even knowing where the towing hook at the front of my car was. Fiona, meanwhile, was happily taking more pictures to add to her scrapbooking account of our holiday escapades.

With assistance we eventually got out of the mud and made it to the road. The passing of time was such that we felt obliged to say our goodbyes all over again. While doing so, I overheard one of the onlookers comment empathetically to my mother, "He really didn't need this, not with everything else as well."

Somehow, my cancer had, at least in her eyes, exonerated me from blame. I'm not sure Fiona would agree.

FROM:	**FIONA MAGGS**
DATE:	**10 SEPTEMBER 2007**
TO:	**OUR NETWORK OF FRIENDS AND FAMILY**
SUBJECT:	**UPDATE ON THE MAGGS FAMILY**

Well, here I am, Monday morning and on my own in the house at the moment! A number of people have been asking what is going on so I thought it was time to bring people up to date.

The good news is (and there is no bad news!) that Chris started his return to work on Wednesday last week. He is just working three mornings a week at the moment 9.30 - 1.00 to ease him back in to the work environment. His hours will then gradually be increased every couple of weeks with an extra half day. He found his two mornings last week tiring but is back there this morning trying to sort through his many emails. As he has only worked for a few months (when he started his return last year) since May 2005 it is quite a challenge for him.

The last time we visited the hospital the Consultant was pleased with the most recent CT scan. They are continuing to monitor Chris with blood tests and examinations every three months and so we are now in a 'wait and see what happens' situation. They are not able to give us any assurances that the last treatment completely got rid of the cancer although Chris has recovered from his stem cell transplant well. His bone marrow is now working properly although this treatment will have an impact on him for up to 18 months mainly with continuing tiredness. We will be back at the hospital again next month.

The rest of the family continue to grow and get older. Tim will be going back to Portsmouth University next Monday to start his second year. He has fallen in love and so we now have Esther who he will be leaving behind - much more stressful than leaving his Mum last year! Luke was very successful and managed to get a clutch of A's and A's for his GCSE's and has started in the 6th form at school to do his A levels. Hannah also started at secondary school last week. She looks very grown up in her tie and blazer and seems to be enjoying it so far. I am increasing my working hours as I have taken on the administration of a four hospital drug trial. Next week I will also be starting on an 'Expert Patient' course which runs for 6 weeks.*

Hope that has brought you all up to date. Chris and I continue to be very involved in our church, both of us being part of the leadership team. We will be celebrating our 5th church anniversary on 23rd September. We have and still do appreciate all the prayers and messages that we receive from everyone. Our faith has been a major part of getting through the last few years (it is almost three years since Chris started to be ill). Although it has been very tough at times I believe that without the prayers of everyone and without the constant protection and unfathomable peace that God has given us, things could have been much worse!

With much love to you all, Fiona

STILL CARRYING THE TORCH

So we came towards the conclusion of another stage in our family's journey. As before, it was both encouraging and daunting to be going back to work. Encouraging, obviously, because it meant sufficient health and strength to resume normal activities. Daunting because normal things, like getting up earlier to go to work, driving through rush-hour traffic, walking through the office and seeing familiar faces, all carried a heavy significance that did not used to be there. The tag of 'cancer victim' (or perhaps now 'cancer survivor') hung self-consciously around my neck.

As before, my work colleagues and the insurance people who are responsible for my long-term sickness payments were extremely understanding. A gentle progression of hours over four months allowed me to ease back into the routine at a steady pace. I had a different expectation this time too. Perhaps when I returned to work last year I imagined I could take back old responsibilities rather quicker than I actually did. This time, with the passage of another year, I had more realistic expectations. As a result, I was pleased at how much involvement I was able to have in the first few weeks, developing new business, taking on client responsibilities and managing a team of people.

Of course, there were a few technical hiccups along the way. It seemed the computer system was less understanding than my human fellow-workers. I received a number of unsympathetic messages from my machine, starting with the rather abrupt, "Account Disabled". Is that still politically correct? Shouldn't it say, "Account with Disabilities" or even "Ability-challenged Account"? Another message informed me I had "fallen off the network". Ouch!

But my favourite message was, "The trust relationship between this workstation and the primary domain has failed." It made me smile and feel sad at the same time. I've never particularly thought of computers having trust relationships but, since they apparently do, a loss of trust must be a heavy load to bear. Sadder still, when I reported the problem to our helpdesk they decided that since they were rolling out new hardware they would not fix the problem, just give me a new workstation. So my old one was taken away still bearing the shame of a broken relationship that was never restored. I imagine it, even now, sitting all alone in some storeroom searching its circuits in vain, hoping to find a reason for its cruel banishment.

At the same time as getting back to work I was also able to get back to a number of other things as my health improved. Our church life is an important part of our family activities and Fiona has agreed to take on more of the administrative work needed to keep everything going. I was pleased to have a friend volunteer to help me restart our church drama group, with Luke and Hannah both involved too. The danger we ran was trying to take on too much and neglecting time to just be family together. Much as I love being part of a church it can quickly consume time and when I noticed that in one week I had arranged four evening meetings, all at our house, I made a mental note to try and keep things in balance!

One thing I agreed to do in October was a little talk at the Wolverhampton Torch Trust for the Blind. This is a Christian organisation aimed at giving practical and spiritual support to the blind community. Fiona's mother has been involved in the organising committee for many more years than she cares to remember and she asked if I'd talk at one of their Saturday afternoon meetings. I was happy to do so, but when I stopped to think I realised I knew very little about what Torch was like. I knew the name very well but mainly in connection with food. The committee lay on sandwiches and cakes after each meeting and Fiona's mum has always been a substantial provider of provisions. The leftovers frequently find their way to our table and so I probably knew more about what Torch people ate than who they were.

In my mind, knowing your audience is vital to preparing any talk, so I checked with the mother-in-law what sort of thing they might be looking for. She said that they had been following my progress over the course of my illness and praying for me regularly, so all I really needed to do was talk about what had happened and how God had been with me. It was an easy assignment. I can talk about myself all day. Unfortunately, I only had ten minutes.

Actually, when it came down to it, thinking what I wanted to say was not so easy, especially when it came to thinking about what I've learned. Experiences are great lessons for us all but the curriculum of life does not generally require us to distil them into ten-minute talks. Perhaps that is a shame. We might learn a great deal more about ourselves if we spent time every now and again pausing to contemplate. Or maybe we'd all become self-obsessed and spend ages writing accounts of our lives for public consumption. Hmmm.

When the big day came, Fiona and I travelled over to St. Jude's church hall in Wolverhampton, accompanied by Hannah. Many of the group were elderly. Some had lost their sight with age, others had been blind or partially sighted for much or all of their lives. Many came with friends who were sighted but who were very much part of the group too. There was a strong sense of community among them and a welcome for all. They were a comfortable group of people to be with. It opened my eyes (forgive the pun) to some things I would not have thought about otherwise, such as:

- how meaningful touch can be in communication. Holding a hand during conversations allows physical expressions of emphasis through slight movements that would normally be conveyed by body language and facial expressions;

- the difficulty of knowing who is there when they meet. It surprised me at first when a register was called as part of the meeting. It seemed incongruously formal. But then I realised that for those unable to see it not only told them who was present but also let them map out where everyone was as they called back from different parts of the hall;

- the value of a smile. When I stood up to speak there was one man who sat near the front with such a broad smile on his face it gave me great encouragement. He was blind himself, with other health problems besides, but he carried such a happy demeanour he lifted my spirits just by being there.

The calling of the register also included the opportunity to update everyone on several people who could not be there that week or had other news. Absence was often due to health problems but not exclusively. Sometimes it was a family event or a trip to visit friends. All of the news was shared and received with such interest that I felt humbled to realise that my developing story would have been passed on over many past meetings and they would have taken it to heart and then to prayer as they did today. These were not people who would be viewed in any usual sense as powerful or important and yet they represented to me a battalion of believers engaged in the serious business of spiritual living by being a Christian community together.

Afterwards I spoke with a number of them about their own experiences of life. By comparison, for all my 45 years, I was still in the flush of youth. All could tell of hardships they had endured, though few even referred to their lack of vision as one of them. It was good to hear story after story of how they had felt God's presence in difficult times. My own story felt like just a drop in the pool of their combined experiences but it was good to see its ripples bringing reminders to them of God's faithfulness. One lady told me how, as a teenager, she had faced the probability of death in a hospital bed as a result of cancer. The doctor had told her there was little chance she would survive. She had a strong faith and told God she was ready to be taken. She survived. Now frail and in her nineties she quipped, "And I've told him a number of times recently I'm ready too and he still hasn't taken me".

I've often thought how good it is we cannot foresee the future. We have enough trouble coping with the past and the present, how on earth would we manage the future too? My own future was interestingly balanced. According to the doctor there was a 50/50 chance that the treatment I received would have been fully successful. If it was then I may well live to my nineties too and be waiting hopefully for the final bus home. On the other hand, if it wasn't successful then there are no other mainstream alternative treatments. New ideas are always in development but the chances of success are lower still. The two scenarios are such extremes and it all rests, it seems, on the same level of chance as a flip of a coin.

Which brings me, in a round about sort of way, to what I did actually talk about at the Torch Fellowship. After briefly explaining my story, I came up with four main things I'd say I've learned along the journey.

1. What a wonderful wife I have. Fiona has been such a constant companion and source of strength, I admire her more than ever for the way she has cared for me.

2. That the theory of Christian faith works out in practice. As I have mentioned before, I had an understanding of how hardships fitted into the big picture and how God was able to deal with us through them but when it came to the crunch would it all hang together? It did, and is more real to me for having done so.

3. That in the most difficult and despairing moments, I found God to be at the foundation of my life. It's never nice to go there but when you've had everything else stripped away you know that what is left is real. When I hit rock bottom it was great to find that God was there – and there in a more tangible way than when life is full of the usual stuff.

4. That God's love is expressed both physically and spiritually through his 'body', the church. The acts of kindness shown by family and friends are the presence of God in the physical world and their support in prayer engages a spiritual dimension we have yet to fully understand. We need look no further when we ask where God is in suffering.

And as a result of the things I've learned I am confident to trust in God for the future, regardless of the outcome.

PART THREE

MATTERS OF THE HEART

MATTERS OF THE HEART

After our journey in 2005 to 2007 through the trauma of cancer treatment, life was fairly routine. At least, that was the case until August 2009 when I suffered a cardiac arrest. It is no exaggeration to say I would have died if circumstances had been a little different. Whatever the downsides of ill health, at least it makes life a tad more interesting and worthy of extending the account of our family's adventures!

Although this is a much shorter trip than previously, I hope it provides further insight into our little world and the things that matter to us. You already know that one of those things is our faith in God. As creator of life, human beings and specifically hearts, there might be some justification in questioning his divine plan in the midst of the events we are about to describe. Well, he does feature in the account and you will find out how we feel about his involvement.

A quick update on the family front in the summer of 2009. Our oldest son Tim had just finished a 'year out' working in London for a computer games development firm and was preparing for his final year at Portsmouth University. Second son Luke had just got his A-level results on 20 August. Rumours that they were sufficiently shocking to cause my cardiac arrest the following day are totally unfounded. He did really well and secured a place to study bio-medical science at Sheffield University. Our daughter Hannah had grown into a beautiful, elegant (and sometimes moody) young teenager ready to start back in year 9 when school holidays ended.

The summer had passed in typical British fashion, with occasional sun and plenty of rain. I was back to working full time and Fiona was holding several roles together including part-time research therapist, church administrator and household manager. You never know what is around the next corner though.

FROM:	FIONA MAGGS
DATE:	23 AUGUST 2009
TO:	OUR NETWORK OF FRIENDS AND FAMILY
SUBJECT:	UPDATE ON CHRIS

Hi to everyone,

Unfortunately I seem to be in a situation for another update on Chris. A few people have been asking me if I was going to do an email as he is unwell again.

The news is that on Friday evening just after he returned home from work he collapsed with a heart attack. We are not sure at the moment why this has happened. He collapsed in front of me so I was able to do artificial respiration (CPR) with help from Tim until the ambulance arrived and they managed to get his heart going. He went in the air ambulance to Walsgrave hospital (it landed in the field behind our house). There he was put on a ventilator and has been in the Intensive Therapy Unit for a couple of days.

This evening they have taken him off the ventilator and when I left the hospital he was managing to breath on his own, although he is still rather drowsy and confused. When he is stable enough he will be moved to be looked after by the cardiologists in the coronary care unit. They will have to try and assess what has happened and work out what needs to be done, which may involve heart surgery.

I know that many people who had already heard have been praying for him and the rest of the family. We do appreciate all the prayers, offers of help and hugs. Chris has a long way to go to recover and he has been through so much already that his body is fragile. God has already been in what has been a difficult situation and there are many examples of the right person being in the right place just at the right time. Friday night has to be my worst night ever and I thought that Chris was dead. The ambulance team managed to shock his heart into working again and I have to believe that God has let him come back for a purpose and that he will be restored to us in time.

Thank you again for your concerns and prayers.
Love Fiona x

SAVED FOR A PURPOSE

Fiona has a wonderful way of capturing the facts in her emails, without going overboard on the emotion of it all. She comes across as a very 'together' person even in extreme circumstances and indeed she is. So her comment, "Friday night has to be my worst night ever and I thought that Chris was dead", makes me stop and ponder just how awful an experience it was for her. And I do have to stop and ponder because I have no recollection of it whatsoever. Although I was a central character, I had to be told the story myself. It was as if I was hearing about somebody else and every now and then I needed to be reminded it was me.

The story had to be told to me many times. My memory was poor and I kept forgetting things, so Fiona and others took me through it lots of times, which meant I kept discovering new aspects as I built up the picture and created my own artificial 'memory' over the following few days and weeks.

I do remember the events running up to my collapse. A few weeks before, I had experienced some quite severe chest pain. It happened at the end of an evening of playing table tennis, table football and pool with my brothers and our lads. In fact, it was the final game of the evening and there was quite a bit resting on the outcome as I took on my younger brother, Joe, at ping-pong. A win for me would see me unbeaten at this particular game all evening but Joe was a tough competitor and it was a pretty even contest. Half way through the match I had this sensation, later confirmed as angina, that started in my chest and spread slowly down my left arm and up into my neck. Pains are always difficult to describe but the best I can do is say it seemed as if the area was being frozen, but without the coldness. Everything felt like it was tightening up and it was harder to breathe.

Of course, the sensible thing would have been to stop the game and rest. But I was slightly ahead and any sign of weakness might have lost the psychological advantage so I foolishly played on through the discomfort. After a few minutes the feeling started to decrease and eventually went away. More importantly, I won the game! Competitive? Me? Actually, I have to record that Joe won the overall competition due to his prowess on the pool table and a dodgy scoring system that favoured the cue over the bat, but I'm not bitter.

As is my usual approach to problems, I did not worry about the pain I had experienced on the basis that it was unlikely to be anything significant. If ignored it would probably go away. It did not. I experienced it again, playing tennis a week or so later. This was another 'crucial' match, the semi-final of our tennis club singles competition and, despite the odds, I was up in the first set against a much younger player. Again, I played through the pain, as we professionals do, and it went away.

However, in the next few weeks the same feeling started getting more frequent – at first just during exercise but then at other times too, once when I was just lying awake in bed. I consulted a medical expert (Fiona) and she booked me in to see the GP the following Saturday morning. I never got that far.

Friday 21 August was a fairly typical day at the office. At the end of the day I rounded off a few loose ends, completed my timesheet for the week and drove home. It was a sunny day and Fiona was out in the back garden tidying up a flowerbed. I went out to find her and told her I was having another of those pains. I sat down on one of the garden chairs to let it pass. When it did, I got up to say I was feeling better and I would make a cup of tea. Then my heart stopped pumping, I collapsed unconscious and started going blue.

Fiona's actions in the next few minutes saved my life. If she had just called an ambulance I do not think I would have survived. She shouted for Tim to come – a shout that Tim, sitting in his bedroom some distance away, not only heard but understood to mean, "This is an emergency, get here right now!" Apparently, it was so loud that Fiona had a sore throat for days afterwards. And then she did CPR. Now I'm not even sure I would know what CPR stands for, let alone be able to do it. It's the sort of thing you see actors doing on TV, banging on the chest, mouth to mouth resuscitation and so on. She had learnt it at work as part of the standard NHS training, but had never done it for real. Somehow, she was together enough to remember the process and keep me going while Tim called the ambulance.

The 'fast response' paramedic and an ambulance both arrived within ten minutes or so. This in itself was either a miracle or a coincidence, depending on your point of view. The local ambulance service only operates during the day and they told Fiona that they should have gone home. However, as they were still at the station when the call came through they responded. If they had not been there it would have been referred through to Bromsgrove and taken a lot longer for help to arrive. Delay might have made the difference between life and death or at least some permanent brain damage due to lack of blood supply to the brain.

We are not entirely clear at what point the air ambulance got invited to the party but it added to the drama having a helicopter land in a nearby field. By this time the ambulance people had used electric shock treatment to get my heart back into rhythm. Once stabilised, they put me onto a trolley. I was then wheeled through the garden, up the drive, along the pavement to the farm three doors down and into the field. What the neighbours thought I cannot imagine!

As I said before, I knew nothing of this until it was recounted to me days later. As I listened I felt somewhat detached from the character on the trolley. When I got home, Hannah showed me the clothes the paramedics had taken off me. There were my trousers and shirt, crudely cut off in the rush to treat me. Later, Fiona found my shirt buttons in the garden, popped off when my shirt was torn open. It really brought it home to me how dramatic the episode had been. It seemed a shame that I had missed it.

As well as Fiona, particular credit goes to Tim for coping well in a crisis and showing maturity beyond any we have seen in him before. He sorted out calling the ambulance, meeting them and bringing them round the back, looked after his sister (who he told to stay upstairs) and gave support to Fiona throughout. He and his girlfriend Esther have now booked themselves on a first aid course. Perhaps they are assuming, with my record, that I will have need of their assistance at some stage.

Luke, I should mention, was not around when all this activity was taking place. He was playing tennis. The first he knew about it was when our neighbour turned up at the tennis club to tell him he needed to go home because of an emergency. Knowing Luke he would have been disappointed to leave a tennis match mid-game but he returned home to keep vigil during the evening with Tim. Hannah went to spend some of the evening with our other neighbours, while Fiona travelled to the hospital in Coventry where I had been flown.

Sometime later, when Fiona was explaining the events to me for the umpteenth time, I remember asking her if she had been worried. She left me in no doubt! I was understanding it all from the perspective of having survived and beginning to feel a lot better. At the time, she explained, I might have died before the ambulance arrived, during the journey to hospital, or at any point over the next few hours in intensive care. Even when I was fully stabilised I was still unconscious and there was no way of knowing what damage might have been done.

Remarkably, I seem to have come through without any permanent mental complications, or at least no new ones. This I put down largely to the hands of Fiona and God. Fiona kept me alive by pumping my chest aggressively until the ambulance arrived – so aggressively that for months afterwards it was sore – but I believe that the hand of God was also present. If I had collapsed when nobody was there, or even in the car as I drove home, I would be dead. If the ambulance people had gone off shift when they should have done it seems unlikely that help would have arrived in time. And these are just the things I can see.

What other ways God may have directed things in the background will remain unknown.

Of course, with this line of thinking it does beg the question as to why God did not intervene to avoid it happening altogether. He could have corrected the defect before it got to this stage. And why would he intervene to save me while other people die in similar circumstances? I do not have the answers to these questions. All I can say is that I see God in the things that happened to me and I am thankful for that.

A number of people have said, and Fiona even put it in her email two days after the event, that I have been saved for a purpose. Wow! This puts the pressure on. I'm now obliged to do something significant with my life. Well, we'll see. As far as I am concerned, my purpose is to live my life as well as I can. Whether that amounts to much in other people's eyes is not important. At the end I anticipate standing before God and I think it's his measure of what is significant that matters.

Jesus told a story about servants who were given 'talents' by their master before he went away for a while. When he came back he commended those who had used them and chastised those who had not. I may not change the world but if I can achieve the accolade the master used, "Well done good and faithful servant", I will be well chuffed.

FROM:	**FIONA MAGGS**
DATE:	**25 AUGUST 2009**
TO:	**OUR NETWORK OF FRIENDS AND FAMILY**
SUBJECT:	**NEXT INSTALMENT ON CHRIS**

Yesterday Chris was moved off the ITU and into CCU (coronary care unit) and he has now got rid of many of his tubes and drips. He is rather confused still and has little short term memory at the moment. He sometimes seems to know he is in hospital although has no idea why or that there is anything wrong. I explained numerous times as have the nurses but 10 minutes later you can tell him again!

There is only one short visiting time in the evening so I have not been able to make any contact with the medical team looking after him. I have phoned and asked to speak to someone so hopefully at some point they will phone me and I will either talk on the phone or make an appointment to go and see someone. Until that happens, I have no idea of what is going to happen next.

Please continue to keep him in your prayers. He was starting to complain of his chest hurting last night and he is coughing. Due to all his previous cancer, surgery and radiotherapy his chest is damaged already and any infection tends to be more difficult to shift. The children and I seem to be coping and all managing to sleep OK at the moment - mainly by keeping busy. Thanks for all the messages of encouragement and good wishes.

Fiona

HOLIDAY HICCUPS

For several years now the joke in our family is that whenever a holiday is planned, I am the cause of us not being able to go. I would like to say this is grossly unfounded, but unfortunately it is not.

The first holiday mishap occurred several years before my cancer, when we missed our main summer holiday because of a parachute jump. It was a sponsored event that a friend and I undertook with all good intentions. There was a day of training and then a solo parachute drop to finish. Everything went fine with the training. While my feet were on firm ground I did fairly well. The trouble started when we headed skyward in a small plane.

There were five of us crammed into the hold as we gradually gained height and the plane began to manoeuvre into the right position. Of course, this involved a fair bit of banking as the pilot was trying to stay over the airfield. I have never been a great traveller, as my Dad knows from the number of times I used to be sick in his car as a child. Planes are far worse, and by the time we were at the right height I was feeling decidedly queasy.

This did have one advantage. Most people might be a little nervous about pushing themselves out of an aeroplane into thin air. Not me. I was desperate to get out! I only wished I could have gone first but I was squashed in at the back of the hold so was last in line to jump. We circled around two more times before my turn and I became increasingly nauseous. It was only a matter of time before I would throw up if I did not get out of there fast.

When my turn finally came I pushed myself out of the plane and had the most wonderful feeling as the nausea left me almost immediately. Even better, my parachute deployed and I began the inevitable process of drifting earthwards. This is the bit everybody raves about – that amazing sense of just floating in the air. Unfortunately it was spoiled for me when, moments after leaving the plane, and despite the sickness feelings having gone, I threw up dramatically.

To say the least, this detracted from the experience somewhat. Floating weightlessly through the air is one thing, floating weightlessly through the air while covered in vomit is another. In normal circumstances, gravity takes the bulk of the stomach's output downwards and out of the way but because I was also falling through the sky a good proportion of it got stuck to me. This unfortunate turn of events is my excuse for what happened next.

The main thrust of the training had been about how to land. Falling is easy, landing is the tricky bit. They did explain that as you get closer to the ground your sense of speed has to readjust very quickly and you need to be concentrating so that on impact you let your legs fold under as you perform a smooth roll over to achieve a graceful landing. They did not mention what to do if distracted by being covered in sick. The ground came up at me very fast and I fell clumsily in a heap, my back taking the brunt of gravity's wrath. Initially I felt no pain but then I realised this was because I could feel nothing at all.

Meanwhile, the wind got hold of my parachute and started pulling me along the ground. We had been warned about this and I was able to reel in the material by reaching over my head while still lying on my back and tugging it all towards me into a bundle. Having done that I was stationary again but still lacking feeling below the waist.

We had been fitted with radios so that, if necessary, we could receive instructions as we descended. I now heard the instructors asking me to get up and indicate I was alright. As requested, we had landed at various points in a large field some distance from the airfield buildings and they were now viewing us through binoculars to make sure we were making our way back, beaming elatedly at the transcendent experience. Perhaps they thought I was continuing to lie on my back as I relived the moment. Alas not. I gradually struggled to raise myself onto one side and then, as feeling returned, accompanied by serious pain and heavy-duty aches, I very gingerly got onto my feet. Then began the slow and painful walk back, clutching my now sick-stained parachute to my chest.

I could not drive home. My friend, who had enjoyed his jump immensely, did the honours. I was in agony. The eventual diagnosis was that I had crushed two vertebrae at the base of my spine. As a result, our imminent caravan holiday was out of the question, especially as it involved lots of pulling and pushing just to get the caravan set up. So that year we holidayed at home, spending some time each day in the caravan while it sat next to our house.

And then there was the scheduled trip to America in the summer of 2005. Not being big holiday people, this was to be the mother of all holidays. Apart from one camping trip to France we had not been abroad before as a family so everyone was looking forward to it immensely. Unfortunately, my cancer came at just the wrong time and we had to cancel the trip. Instead I spent the summer having chest surgery and then recovering enough to start chemotherapy.

I mention these two disappointments because the sequence continued in 2009. Ever since the cancer, we have been cautious about booking anything too far ahead. So we tend to leave it for a while. Then we leave it for a while longer. Then it's usually too late to book anything.

In 2009 we found that summer had arrived and we had no plans. So we made some last-minute arrangements to spend a few days in Wales with Fiona's sister, the highlight of which was to be a trip to Cardiff to see 'The Sound of Music' featuring the 'How do you solve a problem like Maria?' winner, Connie Fisher. Alas, it was not to be. Hannah was the only one who made it to The Sound of Music', bravely accompanied by other members of

Fiona's family in our place. Our holiday time was spent in Coventry instead.

Tim and Esther had booked to go to a large Christian youth event over the same period but gave up their holiday to keep vigil at my bedside and support Fiona, for which I am very grateful.

So holidays remain an elusive dream – something that other people do. Maybe one day….

FROM:	**FIONA MAGGS**
DATE:	**26 AUGUST 2009**
TO:	**OUR NETWORK OF FRIENDS AND FAMILY**
SUBJECT:	**UPDATE ON CHRIS**

It's late but I will give an update on Chris before I go and lay down my weary head.

Tonight when I got to the hospital there was a doctor and nurse at the bed and I realised something was happening. The doctor was putting in another drip and I noticed that Chris was back on his oxygen. He has developed an infection which they had just started to treat. They picked it up in his urine but he may also have a problem with his chest as he is coughing and it hurts. They are waiting for other results back to confirm any other infection.

Also today, the Consultant phoned me at home to explain what is happening. The confusion and short term memory loss is expected in the circumstances and he told me that they are planning to do some tests, an angiogram to start with. This might have been done tomorrow but I think the infection will now delay any tests of this nature. They are also talking about the possibility of an implanted defibrillator which will be wired into his heart and then if it stops again will automatically deliver an electric shock to restart it. (Chris was talking about getting a new heart!) He still can't remember what has happened on the previous day, so I arrived today with him asking why I had not been to see him yet! He has now written down each day he has been in hospital and who has been to see him on each day. It is all rather confusing for him and his grasp of reality fluctuates.

On the positive side, I have been sleeping extremely well for which I am very grateful. Once again I thank you for all your prayers and concerns for our family.

Love from Fiona x

FILLING IN THE GAPS

The memory issue and my general confusion about events keeps coming up in Fiona's emails and it was the cause of amusement for several of my visitors. Weeks afterwards one of my friends asked me if I thought his wife was an angel. I didn't really know how to answer that. After some awkwardness he realised I had no idea what he was talking about. Apparently when he and his wife had visited I was very much of the opinion that she was an angel come to see me.

My two brothers and Fiona were present on one occasion when I started talking about being in the French Secret Service. I have no memory of this whatsoever so am relying on their account but allegedly I made this claim to explain why I was in hospital. Something must have gone wrong on a mission and here I was recovering from a near death experience. Where this idea came from I do not know. I'm not even sure the French have a Secret Service. And I don't speak French beyond 'O' level grade C (second attempt). So I want to make it perfectly clear that I am not and never have been in the French Secret Service. But then again, I would say that wouldn't I.

At the time, though, I was less sure on the matter. Apparently we joked about it for a while and my brothers gave me the code name Pascal. There was a lot of laughter as we talked through various scenarios but some of the frivolity on their part was relief. It acted to counterbalance my brothers' previous visit. They had come to see me in ITU a few days earlier, drifting in and out of consciousness, tubes in every orifice, unable to communicate, occasionally bringing up some bile. At that stage they thought they might have lost a brother. Now they had discovered he was still alive and leading a double life as a secret agent. Even then, the fun was tinged with occasional uncertainty. Did I really think it was true? Would I regain my mental faculties?

When they had gone and I was alone with Fiona I'm told I sought some reassurance. "I'm not really in the French Secret Service, am I?"

My brothers still like the idea though. They have even developed it into plans for a six-part situation comedy under the title 'Wake up call!' Each episode starts with a telephone call waking someone up. The first alerts someone to the fact that Chris, the main character, is in hospital, seriously ill. During visiting, Chris, who is confused, says something about being in the French Secret Service. His family think it is a joke but as the story unfolds there remains this ambiguity. Is he deluded? Is he really a spy? He is not even sure himself. Various things happen to make him think he is receiving coded messages, and the name Pascal keeps cropping up unexpectedly.

How it all ends is not clear but I like the concept. If it comes to fruition I would gladly take on the role of a confused middle-aged professional man fantasizing about dangerous secret exploits – unless Martin Clunes was available.

As for other interesting conversations at the time, Hannah tells me we had a very wide-ranging chat about boyfriends but will not go into details on what was said. Fiona tells me I was surprisingly amorous at times but again a discreet veil is pulled over the dialogue.

All I have to go on is the notes that I scrawled down at the time. They get fairly detailed from 31 August onwards but before that it is basic facts only. Apart from listing visitors the only information I managed to grasp hold of sufficiently to record was as follows.

Friday (21st):	Collapsed after work.
Saturday (22nd):	Unconscious
Sunday (23rd):	Unconscious but then taken off ventilator
Monday (24th):	Moved to coronary care
Tuesday (25th):	No memory

Thursday the 27th of August was our 26th wedding anniversary. I had arranged with Hannah, previous to my collapse, to make a heart-shaped card and she brought this in to me secretly. It was not the most romantic of settings but Fiona and I were grateful to still be together and I probably made some vague promise about making it up to her later with a trip away. Perhaps we could go to Paris, the city of romance. As it happens, I have a couple of little jobs to sort out there, under the name of Pascal.

FROM:	FIONA MAGGS
DATE:	29 AUGUST 2009
TO:	OUR NETWORK OF FRIENDS AND FAMILY
SUBJECT:	UPDATE ON CHRIS

One week has passed by. It was strange yesterday afternoon and evening, I kept looking at my watch and thinking, "This time last week".

Chris is making slow progress at the moment. I think his body will find it difficult to fight due to all the treatment for cancer that it has been through in the past. When I went yesterday they had still not managed to find an antibiotic for the two infections that he currently has. He was about to start a new one at 10.00 last night. The microbiologist had also asked for more samples so they were yet again taking blood (which they have some difficulty in getting from Chris due to the state of his veins). They have had to re-catheterise him as the infection there was causing problems. On Thursday he had two 'funny turns' which were related to these infections. This resulted in him spending all day Friday in bed as he felt too weak to get out and do anything. Not that he can go further than the chair by his bed if he gets out as he is attached to monitors.

Because of the infections, the angiogram that is planned will not happen until Tuesday at the earliest. I'm not sure what else they plan to do yet. However, he is keeping the doctors very busy!

One thing that has improved is his memory. He can now remember that I have been to see him and although he is vague about various things there is a definite improvement. He does keep asking me to repeat what happened and seems quite fascinated that he was 'dead'! I suppose it must be odd having a gap in your memory and knowing you were there when something happened but having no knowledge of it at all.

The children are all doing OK. We celebrated our 26th wedding anniversary on Thursday. For once we had planned something, which is very unusual for us! We were going to see 'Sound of Music' in Cardiff. Hannah went with my mum and sister instead and will be returning today, so I am looking forward to hearing all about it. Tim has gone off to Portsmouth today to sign his contract for the flat he is renting for his last year there. He will be back tonight. Luke has some important tennis matches coming up and has broken a string on his racquet so we are just off to get it re-strung. Life goes on!

Thank you for your interest, concerns and prayers for us all. I know they are keeping us going and protected through this difficult time.

Love Fiona

ANYONE FOR TENNIS?

When Fiona says, "Luke has some important tennis matches coming up", she understates the matter considerably. I am not saying that the Wythall Tennis Club summer tournament should have equal ranking with the Grand Slam events in Australia, the US, France and Wimbledon (though some may disagree) but at the very least I would have thought national TV coverage would be appropriate. It is no easy matter to struggle through two or three rounds against the great and the good of Wythall fame and reach the final. Many is the year I have faithfully entered the competitions – singles, men's doubles, mixed doubles – excitedly written the date of the finals in the family diary (usually with a question mark, admittedly) and dreamed of the glory that might be mine. In all those years I have never got even a sniff of the finals, let alone the possibility of being champion.

Like all good fathers, though, I am happy to live out my sporting ambitions through my children. Tim and Luke have been through the ranks of junior football teams with Dad standing on the sidelines urging them on. I must confess, being an introvert my urging is largely internal rather than external. Rarely would an exclamation pass my lips. Even when they scored a goal, and they frequently obliged, polite clapping was as demonstrative as I became. But inside it was an entirely different matter. Inside I longed for them to play well, to score, to be hailed man of the match. Inside I was bursting with pride.

My own football career was patchy and, it has to be said, lacklustre. I put this down in part to the fact that we lived in Devon for the first seven years of my life. While young lads in the cities were honing their footballing skills by kicking chunks off each other in the rough and tumble of street football, down in Devon we took to more gentle pursuits. With Torquay United, languishing in the lower leagues, as the nearest serious football club, I never took any real interest in the game.

When we moved to Wolverhampton my priorities changed very quickly. 'The Wolves' were doing fairly well at the time and, with a long tradition of success, had strong local support. In the playground, the ability to control a ball with your feet was paramount and I had a lot of catching up to do.

My big break came during a football match in a games lesson at junior school. As usual, I was put in defence, my only quality being that I was stocky (fat) and could kick the ball quite hard. For some reason, during a period when our team was attacking, I had drifted into the opposition half. Most of our attacking force, and virtually all of the opposition's team, were in the penalty box when one of their defenders kicked the ball upfield. It came towards me and, with nobody else from our team to leave it for, I did what I always did, kicked it as hard as I could.

I still remember the wonder of that moment. I think it happened in slow motion. The ball soared over the heads of the players in the penalty box and dropped perfectly into the top corner of the opposition's goal. It was almost as if I had meant it!

The teacher responsible for picking the school team was impressed. So impressed, in fact, that I was selected for the next match. I cannot remember anything from that game, or the next one. I am sure I did not manage to repeat my long-distance goal-scoring feat and I was dropped again after these two appearances. The one incident I do remember from this short opportunity to represent the school involved a pair of shorts.

We all wore shorts in those days as part of the uniform. One of the two matches I played in was away, so we had got changed at the school we were visiting and then, after the game, we put on our uniform again and went home. It was only when I arrived home that my mother noticed I was wearing somebody else's shorts. It was easy to spot because my shorts were old and scruffy whereas the ones I was now wearing were fairly new and, unlike mine, did not have several holes worn through in the crotch. How I made the mistake I do not know. I can only think that my mind, as a young schoolboy, was not designed to operate at such a practical level. Which is still the case.

My mother took me and the shorts straight back to the school and the changing rooms where the crime had been committed. There we encountered a very forlorn looking boy gaping in horror at the disgusting hole-ridden shorts that were the only pair left. He had obviously not been able to face putting them on and returning home in such a state. The exchange was made and I hope, to make up for the trauma he experienced that day, that he went on to achieve great things in his life.

At senior school I also had a short period in the school team. Again, it was more by accident than merit. The usual PE teacher who ran the team was away for a few weeks and our Geography teacher stepped into the breach. Whatever his qualities, football management was not one of them. During his brief tenure I enjoyed several games as a regular team player (defence), only to be dropped abruptly, and quite properly, when the PE teacher returned.

It was during these senior school years that I developed an interest in tennis. The main attraction was that by opting for tennis during PE, me and my friend could go off on our own to the tennis courts and mess about, instead of joining in whatever group activity was on offer.

I enjoyed the game though, and while never being particularly good, kept playing on and off over the years. As our children grew, we took them to various tennis training activities and it has become a great sport to share with my two sons particularly. The trouble is, as they have got taller, stronger, faster and more intelligent over the years, I have been moving in the opposite direction. So it was only a matter of time before they were better than me.

And so we come back to the present situation, in which Luke played in the finals of the local Club tournament in singles, men's doubles and mixed doubles while I (having been knocked out in previous rounds) sat in hospital not even able to watch. I can, however, report with great pride that he won all three events and brought home a collection of somewhat oversized trophies to adorn our mantelpiece. So the Maggs name is engraved on the cups at last – no thanks to me.

FROM: **FIONA MAGGS**
DATE: **1 SEPTEMBER 2009**
TO: **OUR NETWORK OF FRIENDS AND FAMILY**
SUBJECT: **UPDATE ON CHRIS**

A few more days have gone by and Chris is still in the Coronary Care Unit at Walsgrave. Fighting the infections is taking a long time and he also now is getting more chest pain with very little exertion. Over the last few days he has had more drips, a kidney scan and been put on beta blockers to try and control the erratic heart rate. I thought that I would be telling you that Chris had his angiogram today, but unfortunately the doctors did not feel he was well enough for it. He is hoping that it will be able to go ahead tomorrow.

Although he does not feel well, Chris is now getting bored as he is restricted in what he can do and as he is constantly attached to an ECG machine and a drip. With visiting just being in an evening the wait to see people is long.

The rest of the family is getting along fine as we are in the last week of the school holidays and making sure that everything is sorted for school and university. The daily trips to Coventry have been good with the traffic being not too busy. That may all change next week I suppose when the schools are back. I must admit that by the end of the day I am really tired. My brain is struggling now to think clearly enough to write! So, time for bed.

Thank you for all the concern and faithful prayer for our family. It is keeping us all going.

Love Fiona x

HOME IS WHERE THE HEART IS

Hospitals are fine institutions and the NHS is a proud legacy of our country's Christian heritage but when it comes to being a patient, I'd much rather be at home. Still, since home is where the heart is, and my heart needed to be in the Coronary Care Ward, it was sort of home from home. I was positioned opposite the nurses' station so my main entertainment was watching their comings and goings, listening to their conversations and occasionally witnessing their squabbles. As with previous stays, I cannot help but be grateful for the care of the nurses. They are all different in character but overwhelmingly dedicated to their profession. One stood out for me. A young Asian girl who just had such a happy demeanour, regardless of what she was tasked with.

Having experienced this positive view of nurses during several stays in hospital, I am beginning to wonder if it is partly due to the Stockholm Syndrome. It has been observed that in hostage situations, the captives begin to form bonds with their captors after a while. Deprived of other human contact and being dependent on their captors for everything, they start to become appreciative of their attention, provision of food, any leniency they show and so on.

A hospital stay is not unlike a hostage situation – confined to bed, dependent on nurses for food, drink and basic ablutions. They even control your 'shackles' in the form of drips and wires that prevent you moving around. There is a wonderful feeling of release (and gratitude) when some tube or other is removed to give you greater freedom. Given the choice, I would always choose an NHS ward to the trauma of being held by terrorists but I hope you follow my train of thought.

Other than visiting time the only people I saw outside of hospital staff were other patients. And I saw little of them. Although it was an open ward, the curtains were drawn between the beds so I never saw the person occupying the bed next to me. My trips to the toilet did not take me past anyone either. In fact, the only other patient I saw much of was a guy in a single room next to the nurses' station.

His door was usually open and through it I could observe his activity and he could observe mine. Neither was particularly interesting. Bed to chair, chair to bed, occasional trip to the toilet if mobile. We nodded to each other occasionally, acknowledging our mutual suffering and after a few days we even had a conversation. Admittedly it was a 'man's conversation', lasting no more than a couple of minutes, but it brought us closer together.

I could also see the readout on his heart monitor screen, and presumably he could see mine. So I would keep an eye on how he was doing, listen in to what the doctors said to him and keep up with the progress of his treatment. While my heart rate was consistently high, his was dangerously low. In the end he had a pacemaker fitted to keep it going at all. I don't know that I would even recognise him without his pyjamas on but he was my best friend for those few days.

Now that I was getting more 'with it' I had the problem of occupying myself. Books, puzzles and a DVD player were the main distractions. My reading matter alternated between the Bible and a novel. Actually, since I chose to read again the gospel of Luke, which recounts the life of Jesus, it was not unlike a novel. And after that I read Luke's sequel, the Acts of the Apostles. I confess that I am not particularly good at reading the Bible regularly, so this was an opportunity to immerse myself in the story. I found it an exciting rediscovery of the life of Jesus and his immediate followers.

Earlier in the year I had been on a short course looking at the New Testament and delving further than I have previously into the historical context of the times. It gave a new depth to the storyline and the radical nature of how Jesus behaved.

What I love most about the records of Jesus' teaching is the way he left so much unsaid. If I were the Messiah, I imagine I would have taken great trouble to chronicle my thoughts and set them out in as unambiguous and methodical a way as I could. Not so with Jesus. He did not write any of his teaching down (as far as we are aware) and seemed more than content to leave his meanings hanging in the air. He spoke in parables and images, requiring his listeners to think things through themselves and reach their own conclusions.

This was not a man who forced his opinions on you but engaged you in a dialogue. He was not afraid that you might go off on the wrong track (though of course you might). I get the sense that he trusted God would continue the dialogue long after the sound of his words had faded away. And he was content to let his words be framed and relayed to future generations through the minds and writings of others, confident that it was not just the words that mattered but his Spirit who would be working in and through them. Fascinating.

As for DVDs, I quickly learned that Clint Eastwood spaghetti westerns were a tad too depressing for my frame of mind. I settled into a daily episode of P.G. Wodehouse's 'Jeeves & Wooster' series with Stephen Fry and Hugh Laurie, in which Wooster would consistently get himself into hot water (usually involving the prospect of matrimony) only to be saved at the last minute through a wizard wheeze thought up by Jeeves. Except, at the end of the last episode, even Jeeves could think of nothing more imaginative than jumping off the side of a cruise ship in the middle of the Atlantic Ocean. Drastic measures for drastic times I suppose. Still, the brave duo survived and made it back to good old Blighty. What ho!

Visiting times brought plenty of variety, featuring friends and family. Most surprising among these was a visit from three lads (now men of course) from my old youth group at Dunstall Road Baptist Church, Wolverhampton – Dave, Dennis and Courtney. Apart from meeting Dave once a few years back, I had not seen any of them since those days. They still knew my younger brother though and had heard of my plight so came to cheer me up. It was great to see them and spend a good hour or so talking about 'the old days'.

My parents visited on 31 August and brought a game along to play. My scribbled diary reads, "We played Scrabble and we were all pretty awful. Very tired when we finished." It must have been lifting those heavy tiles. On 5 September they came again and I wrote, "Played Scrabble and I won so it's a sign I'm getting better". Perhaps the medical profession should use Scrabble as a measure of improving health, keeping records of scores alongside blood pressure and heart rate. The old triple word score certainly sets my pulse racing!

Family members also brought me fruit in abundance, which was a great supplement to the hospital diet when I felt well enough to eat. A particular favourite was grapes – just thought I'd mention it for future reference.

FROM:	FIONA MAGGS
DATE:	3 SEPTEMBER 2009
TO:	OUR NETWORK OF FRIENDS AND FAMILY
SUBJECT:	UPDATE ON CHRIS

Yesterday the angiogram was finally done. Chris had been getting worse over the last couple of days with increasing chest pain and was put into bed and told not to move in the end. I think the doctors decided that they needed to do the tests urgently despite the infections. Anyway the tests showed that one of the coronary arteries has gone into spasm and this is preventing the blood flow in his heart (that is my understanding from Chris' explanation). There was no actual blockage from any narrowing of the arteries.

This problem could not be sorted with a stent (a support tube placed in the artery) but they can use drugs to prevent the spasm. They started him on these yesterday. This spasm may be related to his cancer and treatment. There is also some damage to the heart but I am not sure if this is from the heart attack or from the cancer. I will phone and ask for an appointment with the consultant to find out the details.

We now seem to be heading in the right direction with an answer to why all this has happened. There are still many questions to ask and I am not sure what the future looks like. Hopefully over the next few weeks we will find out, the drugs will work and Chris will begin to feel much better.

I hope that all that makes sense. I am not sure that I fully understand what is happening at the moment but we seem to be making some progress. God is good and I am so grateful that I still have my husband alive. It could so easily have been a different story. Luke is now making his plans to go away to Sheffield University in a couple of weeks and Tim will also be back to Portsmouth. Hannah is back to school on Monday and life goes on........

Thank you for all your messages and for praying for us faithfully. Our faith does not give us a get out clause from the difficulties of life but it does give us an ability to cope with them.

Love from Fiona x

THE 'GET OUT' CLAUSE

I was thinking about Fiona's idea of a 'get out' clause for people of faith. I think God might word the contract terms something like this.

1. *In view of and in proportion to the faith of the contract holder (hereinafter referred to as "The Believer") it is hereby agreed that matters of ill-health, accident and misfortune (erroneously referred to as "Acts of God" by libellous insurance underwriters) shall be treated in the following manner for such period as The Believer shall maintain said faith in accordance with the standard prescribed in paragraph 5 hereunder.*

2. *Ill health shall be restricted to levels of mild discomfort and inconvenience such as colds, short-sightedness and athlete's foot. At the onset of any more substantial ill-health condition, The Believer shall be entitled to utter a prayer of supplication for removal of said condition forthwith. God reserves the right to delay removal of the condition for a reasonable period in order to gain greater publicity and retains the rights to all miraculous claims.*

   The Believer shall be entitled to immunity from suffering resulting from accidents to the extent that The Believer has not in any way, shape or form been the cause of said accident through an act of wilful recklessness or abandon. God will be the final judge and arbiter on such matters.

4. *Similarly, The Believer may call for the removal of misfortune, other than any misfortune experienced as a result of personal greed, avarice, lust or other such sinful behaviour which shall remain the responsibility of The Believer until such time as it is fully repented of by earnest confession submitted in triplicate via the appropriate channels.*

5. *Faith shall be deemed sufficient if it is accompanied by works. However, this shall not be taken to mean that works are sufficient on their own.*

6. *Loss of faith will result in termination of this contract with immediate effect, other than in the case of Calvinists for whom special terms have been negotiated.*

7. *God agrees to abide by this contract only in so far as it does not fetter his divine right to omnipotence. Actions taken by God in accordance with this contract shall therefore be deemed acts of grace.*

Personally, I prefer to have a relationship with God rather than a contract. For a start, I know which of us would be most likely to fall foul of the small print. And I have no pretensions to trying to hold God down to a set of rules or behaviours. C S Lewis' Narnia books portray God as a wild lion who comes and goes as he wills. Nobody can capture him or tame him but he willingly allows some of the children to play with his mane and ride on his back.

To my mind, God, by nature, is uncontainable and not accountable to me for his actions. But where does that leave me (and others) when we are facing suffering?

I like the image of God inviting us into a dance with him. Now that the boys have gone to university and there are more women than men in the house for the first time, our lives have started to become shaped around the TV programme 'Strictly Come Dancing' in which celebrities learn to dance with professional dance partners. It is an interesting parallel with how I understand the Christian faith.

God invites me to enter a dance with him even though he knows I am well short of the standard he would want me to be. He patiently teaches me the steps, by his Holy Spirit working right alongside me and encouraging me. He takes great pleasure in my efforts and enjoys my faltering attempts because he can see my desire to improve. None of his followers get to a perfect standard, there is always more we could do but we can learn so much and come such a long way. And there are many different dances – more to discover, more to challenge and stretch our faith and understanding. And the best thing of all is that, unlike the TV programme, nobody gets voted out each week. Instead, new people come and join the dance.

So what has this got to do with the suffering we experience in life? Well, one way of looking at it is that every experience we have is an invitation to dance a different dance with God. Some are not easy. The celebrities on the TV programme often refer to the difficulties they have in learning a new dance but none of them complain that it is too much or too demanding. In fact, the harder they work at it and struggle to achieve the best they can, the more they seem to gain from the experience.

Now I am not suggesting for one minute that every painful experience is because God wants to teach us a new dance step. I recognise that many people suffer horrendously in their life and I do not want to trivialise the pain and suffering in the world. All I am trying to get across is that for me, when I have difficulties, I recognise God not as the cause of my suffering but as my companion in the suffering. He chooses to come alongside me in whatever situation I am in and walk through it with me – sometimes carrying me when I cannot go on. He does not offer me a 'get out' clause; instead he himself is willing to 'get in'.

FROM: **FIONA MAGGS**
DATE: **5 SEPTEMBER 2009**
TO: **OUR NETWORK OF FRIENDS AND FAMILY**
SUBJECT: **UPDATE ON CHRIS**

Chris continues to improve and after two weeks in hospital he is now well enough to be bored and fed up! The doctors have made a decision on the next part of his treatment and he is to have an operation on Tuesday. This will be to put an ICD (Implantable Cardioverter Defibrillator) in his chest. This is similar to a pacemaker and will monitor his heart rhythm. If it senses any alteration it can deliver a number of treatments from low-voltage electrical impulses to correct the heartbeat, to a big shock if the heart goes into the fatal rhythm it did a couple of weeks ago. If everything goes well he may be discharged within a few days. He will also continue on the drugs.

This will present us with some new challenges as Chris will be unable to drive for 6 months. He should however be able to start returning to work after 4-6 weeks. There are various things he has to avoid. Standing in shop doorways is to be avoided! In fact anywhere with any electromagnets. We have an appointment with the arrhythmia nurse on Monday morning to talk through things.

There will be many appointments and follow ups in the future but it is good to know that they have found a cause and that the solution should be able to give us confidence to live without the worry of it happening again - especially if he was alone. (The information booklet does say that he should not go on holiday to any isolated places!) Please pray for Tuesday that everything will go to plan. We are also fortunate that the doctor who will be doing the operation is actually on holiday next week but is coming in specially to do this and a few other operations on Tuesday (I have imagined the scene in his house!) Otherwise Chris could have been waiting for a week or two for the operation.

Thank you once again for your support and prayers.
Fiona x

DON'T BANK ON IT

One of the wonders of our modern age is the development of impersonal, disjointed organizations providing most of our needs. These include vast supermarket chains, insurance conglomerates, global brands and, of course, banks. Long gone are the good old days of a personal service provided by staff and a local manager who knew you by name and could deal with any issue that arose. Now everything in these organizations is managed through specialist departments so that they can 'process' customers more rapidly, often by telephone or internet rather than face to face.

A lot of the time this approach does have benefits but, unfortunately, it falls apart when an issue crops up that does not fall neatly into one of the allocated boxes. On those occasions the customer is shunted from pillar to post as nobody has sufficient overall knowledge or authority (or desire?) to deal with the problem.

Fiona had one of these experiences over the weeks surrounding my health problems and I think it's a tale worth telling as it demonstrates how life carried on in its normal frustrating way.

It started in August when we received a bank statement notifying us that we were overdrawn. The strange thing was that this is an account we have never used. It was set up when we took out a mortgage and the provider required that, as part of the deal, we had to have an account with them. We told them we didn't want it and would not use it but they insisted it was a condition of the mortgage. So for many years we left it dormant, receiving occasional statements showing a zero balance.

The provider was duly swallowed up by a bigger bank and the name of the account changed but we continued to leave it alone as it did not seem to be doing any harm. So we were surprised to discover in the August bank statement that a direct debit had been set up on the account and we were £9.99 in the red. There followed a series of visits to the bank to sort it out.

Visit one – Fiona went to point out the error. As is typical of banks these days, there are few cashiers and when you do speak to one, the range of things they can do is restricted. Anything vaguely complicated requires a 'personal adviser' (as opposed to an impersonal one). The cashier explained that this fitted in the 'too complicated' category.

When she got to see a personal adviser, she was told they would stop the direct debit and that a dispute form would need to be completed to deal with the £9.99 already deducted. If the form was approved, the amount would be reimbursed to the account.

The personal adviser took the details for the form and said it would go through in a few days.

Fiona also asked whether we could close the account and explained the background. She was told there would be no problem closing it, once it was back in balance, as the old rules and connection to the mortgage no longer applied. The bank would inform us when the correction had been made and the account could then be closed. All appeared to be straight forward.

Visit two – Having heard nothing for a month, and despite having to cope with my cardiac arrest and frequent hospital visits, she returned to the bank in September to find out what was happening. There had been limited progress. The direct debit had been stopped but the dispute form to correct the error had not been sent so we were still £9.99 down. Fiona had to go through the dispute form process again. When she asked about closing the account she was told that since it was in our joint names we would both need to come in, to close an account we had never wanted in the first place. Fine.

Visit three – A few days later she checked the account online and, sure enough, the £9.99 had been reimbursed. So in October, when I was well enough, we made a trip to the bank together. This was my first experience of the queuing system that they operated and I was amazed at the tremendous inefficiency. We knew that the cashiers would tell us we needed to see a personal adviser so we did not join that queue. Instead, we waited for a personal adviser, with another two gentlemen, by a large sign saying, "Can I help you?" We could see the advisers beyond were busy so we waited. And waited.

A smartly dressed man eventually appeared and proceeded to refill a box of pens, conveniently ignoring the queuing customers. After rigorously tidying them up and being satisfied that the display of boxed pens met the bank's exacting standards, he moved over to us, producing a beaming smile from nowhere. "Can I help you?" he enquired of the first gentleman. When his problem had been explained the man decided that this required a personal adviser. He asked the gentleman to take a seat and wait until one was available. The same thing happened with the next customer. It was becoming increasingly clear that the answer to the question, "Can I help you?" was "No!".

When our turn came, we explained that we wanted to close an account. The smartly dressed man considered the matter thoughtfully and decided that this was something that could be dealt with by one of the cashiers. We were invited to join that queue instead.

When we got to the cashier, she told us she could not close accounts and we would have to see a personal adviser! We explained that we had been told, by a very smartly dressed man, she could. So she went away to talk to someone. When she came back, she handed us a scrap of paper with the bank account number written on it and asked us both to sign it. She said she would get one of the personal advisers to close the account later when they were free. We were not convinced. It sounded like the kind of thing that would never happen, and we did not want to have to come back again to get it sorted. The cashier decided we really should see a personal adviser if we wanted to sort it out there and then.

So we returned to the personal adviser queue, behind another customer who had arrived while we were talking to the cashier.

Eventually, we were called through and sat down with a very pleasant lady, to whom we told our sorry tale again. "Unfortunately," she explained, "I cannot close your account down because it is in debit by 1p". Apparently, while the erroneous £9.99 debit sat in our account, it had incurred interest of 1p. So although the £9.99 had been reimbursed we were still (just) in debit.

She told us that we would have to complete another dispute form in order to get the 1p reimbursed. Furthermore, she said she could not do this and close down our account at the same time. The 1p correction had to be processed and we would need to come in after that to close the account. We expressed our frustration at this, particularly as we had made a specific trip together for this purpose. "Oh, you don't both need to be here to close the account", she assured us, "one signature will do." We screamed inwardly, imagining the scenario when Fiona would turn up to close the account only to be told that two signatures were needed.

Our personal adviser tried again to be helpful. She suggested we might transfer 1p from another account Fiona held with them as that could be processed immediately and allow us to close the account. But what amazed me was that she had no authority herself to waive even 1p. It had to go through due process, involving paperwork and the turning of many cogs in the banking machine. After further pressing, she decided that if we gave her the authorisation now, she could close the account herself in a few days time, to avoid us making another visit.

So a new dispute form was completed for the reimbursement of 1p. She told us there would be confirmation of the reimbursement via a letter, and then a few days later another letter confirming closure. Sorted at last!

Visit four – We did, as promised, receive confirmation that our 1p debit was reimbursed. We were back where we started at last. But nothing came through about the account closing and it still seemed to be open as Fiona could go online and access it. She returned to the bank two weeks later, somewhat annoyed.

At the, "Can I help you?" sign, a young man advised her that none of the personal advisers were available as they were all on a conference call and would remain so for another half an hour! So, again the answer to the, "Can I help you?" question was a resounding, "No!".

Visit five – A few days later, Fiona returned to attempt once more the seemingly impossible task of closing the account. This time she was privileged to find herself speaking to the assistant manager of the bank. Here was someone with authority who could get things done! Alas, no. The assistant manager informed her that this was an account taken out in conjunction with a mortgage and, as such, it could not be closed while the mortgage continued. Back to square one.

Given everything else that Fiona had to cope with at the time it amazes me that she had the patience and perseverance to follow this convoluted (and ultimately circular) path over several months. What made the multi-visit fiasco worse was the number of messages around the bank proclaiming how much they valued their customers, always put them first and so on. It typifies the gap between management strap lines and actual delivery. The sad thing is that this type of experience is not uncommon across many of the organisations we have to deal with. We have learned to laugh about it and accept it as part of our modern commercialised image-dominated culture but, really! Okay, end of rant. Time to step back to early September again, at which point I was still in hospital.

FROM: **FIONA MAGGS**
DATE: **9 SEPTEMBER 2009**
TO: **OUR NETWORK OF FRIENDS AND FAMILY**
SUBJECT: **UPDATE ON CHRIS**

Thank you to everyone who was praying yesterday. The operation went ahead and Chris had his defibrillator fitted. They were unable to access his veins on the left side of his chest where it would normally be put (due to previous damage from the tumour) and eventually they were able to put it in the right side. This does mean that it is now his right arm that he will not be able to lift for a few weeks until the leads to his heart have imbedded.

He was feeling okay when I saw him last night and was very hopeful that after his day of tests on the defibrillator and chest x-rays today he will be allowed to come home. Hopefully I will have my last trip to Coventry for a while!

Thank you once again for all your prayers, emails, letters, cards and support over the last few weeks. Chris will now need quite a while to recuperate and start to build up his strength and become active again. The doctors have said that he should be able to be back to work in a couple of months and eventually play tennis again. He seems to think that gardening will no longer be allowed though!!!! That is just wishful thinking.

With grateful thanks from all the Maggs family

Love Fiona x

QUESTION TIME

As my faculties returned to normal over the first few weeks, I started to try and understand exactly what had happened in more detail and what it would mean for the way I lived the rest of my life. I play a very compliant role as a patient. The doctor decides what is wrong and says, "You need an ICD". I say, "Thank you very much". It is only after the doctor has gone that I start to wonder what an ICD is, what it will feel like, how it will affect the things I do, whether there are other options and so on.

Now, it would be easy to criticise the doctors for lack of information but the truth is that as a patient, recovering from illness, it takes time for the questions to formulate and probably even longer for the answers to sink in. All the doctors I spoke to were more than willing to answer any questions I raised but the opportunity to speak to doctors is limited. So I was very pleased to have a specialist nurse, called Helen, take the time to sit down and explain things in greater detail. It was Helen who fielded our subsequent questions by telephone and who has co-ordinated different parts of the NHS to get things sorted when necessary.

Of course, the question that I really wanted an answer to is why I had the cardiac arrest in the first place. The doctor's answer was that he thought it was due to spasm in the coronary artery. Okay, I continued, but why did I have spasm in the coronary artery? The doctor smiled at me as if I had asked an impossibly naïve question.

I suppose there are people who research such things but the doctors I spoke to just did the treatment. The body is too complicated to understand all its interactions and the closest anyone got to giving me an answer was that it may have had something to do with damage from my previous radiotherapy, surgery or chemotherapy treatments. If so, it was an unusual complication and something that the doctors would not have been able to predict was about to happen even if they had been monitoring my heart.

A few weeks after leaving hospital I returned to have a check-up with the cardiologist. As is often the case, I did not see the consultant but one of his registrars. By this time I had gathered a stock of further questions to ask but we came away from the check up more confused than when we arrived.

It did not help that the registrar had no idea of my history. He had my medical notes in front of him but had clearly not had time to read them. So a fair bit of the time was used up with us telling him what had happened. The rest of the time was spent with him casting doubt on the consultant's diagnosis! The registrar, possibly eager to get on with the glittering cardiology career he foresaw for himself, said he thought spasm was not the cause of the attack and that I had not really had angina pains, I just thought I did!

He was a bit vague on what had actually happened, presumably because he was still working on his alternative diagnosis theory, which would be unveiled to an astonished cardiology convention in the fullness of time. It just left us confused. He also suggested some changes to my medication but I was not at all convinced he knew what he was talking about and we agreed with him in the end that we would wait and see how the present regime worked out.

By contrast, we had a very positive experience when we went for a check-up on the ICD. By placing some sort of device over the ICD in my chest, the technician could read off all the data recorded on it since its insertion. So he could tell my heartbeat at any time in the last few months. By a few clicks on his mouse he could also switch the device so that it regulated my heartbeat. He told me he would check that it worked by increasing and decreasing the rate, while assuring me he would remain within a reasonable range. I braced myself for a surge of energy but was disappointed to feel nothing.

He also explained some of the programming in my ICD as well. We had previously been told that it cuts in if my heart malfunctions but by now we had more specific questions. Apparently it will not interfere if the heartbeat is below 200 per minute. With heavy exercise I reach about 140 so there is plenty of margin there. Even if the 200 limit is breached, he explained, there are other factors built in, such as the period of time over 200 and also whether it is the upper or lower chamber of the heart affected. I still cannot claim to know all the details but I was pleased that it seemed a pretty sophisticated device.

Hannah told me about a dream she had in the run up to Christmas. My ICD had 'gone off' and I was having convulsions on the floor as it applied a series of electric shocks. In her dream, the ICD was singing, "We wish you a merry Christmas" at the same time. I quite like the idea that some bright programmer had built in a little festive routine to lighten the mood if it went off around Christmas time.

Some of my questions at this appointment were beyond the technician's remit and he readily called for the consultant who fitted the ICD to come down from the ward. He did so and spent a good ten or fifteen minutes answering all our questions and making some sensible adjustments to the medication regime. It was a really helpful session.

Of course, I still have questions that come up every now and then, some of which I don't think I would ever ask the consultant. For example, now I have my ICD is it true I can never die? Can I officially refer to myself as bionic? Should I avoid Kryptonite? I do know I must not hang around in shop doorways where there are magnetic theft devices. Very occasionally, shop alarms seem to go off when I pass through but I never stop to find out if I am the cause.

At a more mundane level, quite a few people have asked me if it feels odd having such a device. Well, most of the time it doesn't, because I don't think about it. I do notice it when I see myself in the mirror though, as it is fairly prominent. It is a bit like having a slim matchbox under your skin. Occasionally I fancy I can hear it working in the quiet of the night – a very faint clicking noise that I can only hear when I breathe out. It may just be my imagination but I still find it oddly reassuring.

FROM:	**FIONA MAGGS**
DATE:	**3 OCTOBER 2009**
TO:	**OUR NETWORK OF FRIENDS AND FAMILY**
SUBJECT:	**UPDATE ON CHRIS**

Time has passed by and yesterday Chris and I realised that I had not done an update for a while. It just shows that when he is at home my routine is completely disrupted!

Chris has spent the last few weeks at home, slowly getting his strength back and gradually doing more and sleeping less (still no gardening!) For the first couple of weeks he had to be careful not to raise up his arm so that the wires of the defibrillator did not get disturbed. We have had a regular routine of visits to doctors for check ups and dressing changing and prescriptions. We are still however waiting for the cardiology follow up and the ICD follow up - they were trying to arrange for this to happen nearer to home but will now be in Coventry. Chris had an oncology appointment on Tuesday in Coventry as well and they have also decided that they are no longer happy to review him in Redditch. The expression used was that Chris had 'freaked out' the consultant!

On Thursday Chris started his cardiac rehab in physio - this time we are allowed to go to Redditch. He will have this twice a week and gradually build up his confidence and stamina. They also have a series of weekly talks afterwards which we attended. It was interesting for me as this is similar to my work so I enjoyed sitting on the other side of the fence.

Things are slowly beginning to take on a new routine and with just the three of us now it is amazing how little washing there is and how long the food lasts! Luke has settled into Uni well (I think) and is trying to get back to study after a number of months of not needing to do anything. Tim is also settled in his flat in Southsea and is close to the Uni and hopefully his work started this week. He has also been able to keep doing some freelance work for the company he worked for last year. Hannah has asked for a mention - she says that she is the 'perfectist' daughter ever. Time will tell.

We expect things to be much the same for a while now although Chris does plan to start going back to work but this will be on a part-time basis and gradually building up. Until he sees the GP next week we do not know when this will start.

Once again, thank you for all your concern and prayers. It surprised me on Thursday when the cardiac nurse told Chris that, with his medical history he must have survived all that for a purpose. That is something that I said in an email a few weeks ago. Maybe one day we will look back and know what that was!

With lots of love, Fiona x

BACK TO THE FUTURE

Recuperation time is an odd period, trying to get the right balance between resting and pushing yourself. I knew I should take things slowly but I wanted to see what I could do. Half my brain thought I was ready to return to work and the other half would rather I went back to bed. My normal routines were not in place so I was always asking myself what to do next. Except, of course, Fiona's normal routines were still there. It's just that she had to do them with me hanging around, like a lethargic puppy, getting under her feet.

It did not help that I could not drive. The rule is that when someone has an ICD is fitted, they cannot drive for six months. They only get their licence back after that if there have been no 'incidents' making it go off. So I was in need of lifts whenever I had to go somewhere – not that I had many pressing engagements in the first few weeks.

One regular trip, though, was twice a week for my physio group session. This was an exercise class for cardiac patients in recovery. Predominantly made up of retired men, we dutifully circled the room to the strains of Shania Twain singing, "Man, I feel like a woman". This was not so much high-impact aerobics as low-impact shuffling but we each did what we could and felt the better for it.

After the warm up we engaged in a series of exercises that are never likely to emerge as competitive sports in the Olympics. They included repeated standing up and sitting down, stepping onto a small box and off again and walking back and forth across the room. There was also some work on exercise bikes and other equipment.

At the beginning, half way through and at the end we would each take our pulse and have it recorded to make sure we were not about to expire. Mine would go from 80 or so up to 130 or 140. This was way higher than most of the other participants and was enough to stir my competitive spirit to modest self-praise, despite the fact that my 'competitors' were all a good deal older than me, many had pace makers that prevented high heart rates and it was questionable whether a high pulse was a good result in any case.

At home I restricted physical activity to emptying the dishwasher, going up and down the stairs occasionally and doing cross-stitch. As in previous recovery periods, I did not feel mentally in the right place to write creatively, which is a shame as I had so much time on my hands.

The return to work was something I felt ready for earlier than I probably actually was. I went in to chat to my boss and we agreed a phased return-to-work plan, starting with three half-days a week and building up to full time over six weeks. It felt fine initially and I was welcomed back by colleagues and repeatedly told not to rush things.

Yet again, they had discovered in my absence that I was not indispensable (always a dangerous thing) and I did not return to all of my former duties. In fact, I took the opportunity to make a permanent move to working four days a week. This was mainly for health reasons but it was also something I had wanted to do for a while, to make space for more writing time.

After a few weeks of working only half-days, my first full day in the office was on a Thursday and included a meeting with a client. The meeting had been rearranged to be in our Birmingham office to avoid me travelling and I am really grateful to both my client, and another firm of advisers involved, who willingly made the journey to accommodate me. The meeting went well and included a working buffet lunch. We finished early afternoon and I returned to my desk to write up some notes. After about an hour I felt some uncomfortable rumblings that quickly developed into nausea. Around 4 p.m. I made for the toilets, where my lunch made a reappearance.

Feeling the better for having dealt with the problem, which I assumed was a dodgy sausage roll or the like, I finished off my work and left at 5 p.m. for the train. One of the results of being unable to drive was the need to become a train commuter for the first time. We had a station half a mile down the road from our home, with a line into the centre of Birmingham. It was a brisk 15 minute walk from the station to the office but this fitted well with the promise I had made to the physio to maintain a daily exercise routine. As I walked to the station that afternoon, I still felt queasy and had a dizzy headache coming on. I hoped that if I was going to be sick again, it would not be on the train. In fact, as a precaution, I visited the station toilets (not something to be taken lightly) to attempt induced vomiting. There was no output.

The train pulled in and I took a seat, noting where the toilet was further up the carriage should I need to use it. At the next stop the train became very crowded with the usual rush hour crowd. Not only was I surrounded but the corridor was now fully blocked with standing passengers, so a quick dash to the toilet would be impossible. I tried to relax and breathe deeply, after all I did not feel too sick as we left the station and I assured myself that the dizzy feeling was probably no worse than before.

As we progressed slowly, I remember urging each station to come soon, thinking that every stop was one closer to home. In the crowded carriage it was getting hotter. I told myself to just breathe slowly and deeply. I tried to convince myself I was not really feeling sick, I just thought I was. I looked around at the other passengers; the man opposite immersed in his book, the lady standing in the aisle with all the bags, staring oddly at me. I must have looked strangely gaunt and pale. I closed my eyes.

Next thing I knew, as I opened my eyes, was that we had stopped. There were less people in the carriage. The man opposite had disappeared. Oh, and I seemed to have sick all down me; on my suit, on my shirt, on my tie, on my trousers, and all over the seat and my shoes and the floor.

I realised I must have passed out temporarily for this to have happened without my knowledge. I felt groggy and groaned a little as I raised my hand to my head. Everyone was looking at me. A lady just leaving the carriage offered me a small pack of tissues. I did not look up but thanked her as I took them.

Moments later the guard arrived. Somebody had obviously told him about the man who had been sick all over his train. He was all for calling an ambulance but I said he should call Fiona. He suggested I get off the train to get some fresh air (and avoid throwing up in his train again). Out on the station platform I could hardly stand up straight and leant my head against the railings. I was sick again.

The guard called Fiona, who quickly gathered some towels and set off in the car for Hall Green station, although she realised on the way to Hall Green that she did not actually know where the station was. Meanwhile, the guard and another passenger had helped me to some seats on the platform, where I was duly sick again.

I felt like the whole train was watching me through the windows, presumably thinking I was drunk or something. I felt really bad about holding everybody up as the guard could not leave me on my own and there were no staff at the station.

Eventually, a couple of passengers (who happened to be from another train line) volunteered to stay with me until Fiona arrived. So after a fifteen minute delay, the train made its way onwards, to the relief of myself and all the remaining passengers.

Fortunately, Fiona found the station without too much difficulty and with the help of the two 'good Samaritan' train operatives, I was assisted over the bridge and to the waiting car. There, some of the sick that had clung stubbornly to my shirt and tie was wiped off and I was taken home, heaving regularly into a plastic bowl Fiona had brought along for the purpose, depositing into it what little remained of the contents of my stomach.

In fact, when we got home, I did not even get out of the car. Fiona stopped for a quick consultation with our GP, after which we went straight to Accident & Emergency. Given my heart problems we did not know how serious the incident may be. We decided not to clean up because I would probably get seen quicker if I turned up in my dishevelled state. This tactic worked pretty well initially, though once installed in a cubicle in A&E we waited many hours, going over medical histories several times with different staff before eventually I was admitted to the Coronary Care Ward for observation, around midnight.

I was only in there for a day. They monitored my heart, took three lots of blood for tests and decided, after due consideration, they could not identify any heart problems. The main concern was why I had blacked out.

They arranged for me to go to Coventry to have my ICD checked on the Monday to see what that might reveal. It did not reveal very much. It identified atrial fibrillation for an hour or so during the incident (top part of the heart) but this is not as serious as ventricular fibrillation (bottom part) and had not triggered the ICD to go off. So it was not clear whether the problem had been caused by my heart or not. At the same time, they could not say whether it had been food poisoning. It turned out that nobody else who had eaten that lunch had been unwell so it seems unlikely.

Perhaps it was just a bug that, in my weakened physical condition, had knocked me back more than it might a healthy person.

They say that adversity is a necessary evil for the true artist to blossom. Perhaps this is why I turned to poetry to capture the anxieties of this episode, penning this masterful piece a few days later.

Sick on a Train

> Hall Green, all green,
> Grey face, yellow stain, caused a scene
> Homeward intent, embarrassment, tissues well meant
> Nauseous pain, delayed the train, never again!
> Made A&E, fast track for me, ECG
> Medical past, going nowhere fast, decision at last
> Hospitalised! (Not surprised)

I picked up my return to work schedule a little slower after that, and arranged lifts rather than take the train for a while. This was partly cautionary but also because I was embarrassed that people on the train would recognise 'the sick man'. Although, I suppose it would have meant I got plenty of space as people avoided sitting next to me. On the first day that I did take the train again, a couple of weeks later, I heard two people behind me talking. One of them was telling the other how a train had been delayed by someone being sick on it. I kept my head down.

THE END IS NIGH

Since the incident on the train back in 2009, my return to health and normality has been fairly mundane. I have maintained a four-day week at work for over a year now and it seems to be working out well. My intent of daily exercise has fallen by the wayside but I do play tennis once a week and I take the train to work occasionally to ensure I do some walking.

Inevitably, after the sort of experiences these last few years have brought, I come back to wondering what the future holds. The possibility of another cardiac arrest is always there. I will need to keep taking tablets daily to reduce blood pressure and stress on the heart, which serves as a constant reminder of what might happen. Although, if I do have another arrest, the ICD is there to cut in and prevent it being a major problem – at least in theory. I do not fancy the idea of being kept going on that basis too frequently though.

My oncologist continues to monitor me for the time being but there is no sign of a return of the tumour. Time moves on and the memories begin to fade.

As an actuary, I get to think about the probability of dying in a professional context. I have sat through some very dull talks on models for predicting mortality levels and almost wished for death to end the boredom. But statistical probabilities and one's own mortality are very different things. My personal death risk is higher than average given my medical history but I might yet make it to 100. As the old actuarial saying goes, never play dice with probability.

One thing I do feel certain of was written in a letter sent to the church in Rome many years ago. Neither death nor life can separate me from the love of God (Romans 8: 38, 39). Death has no sting (though it might smart a bit at the time). I do not seek it but I do not fear it either. Meanwhile, we get on with life and whatever the future holds.